The Little Manual of SUCCESS

By the same author

* The Little Manual of Happiness
* The Little Manual of Meditation
* The Little Manual of Enlightenment

The Little Manual of SUCCESS

9 Essential Secrets of Self-Made Millionaires

Vikas Malkani
Best-selling author of
THE LITTLE MANUAL OF HAPPINESS

UNICORN BOOKS

This edition published by :
UNICORN BOOKS (P) Ltd., New Delhi-110002
J-3/16 , Daryaganj, New Delhi-110002
☎ 23276539, 23272783, 23272784 • *Fax:* 011-23260518
E-mail: unicornbooks@vsnl.com
Website: www.unicornbooks.in • www.kidscorner.in

Distributors
Pustak Mahal, Delhi
E-mail: info@pustakmahal.com • *Website:* www.pustakmahal.com

Year of Publication : 2008

ISBN: 978-81-7806-138-2

Editorial and design: Write Media

Original Edition Published by: SoulWords Publishing Pte Ltd., Singapore
www.soulwordspublishing.com

I have no secret. There are no rules to
follow in business. I just work hard and,
as I always have done, believe I can do it.
Most of all, though, I try to have fun.

Richard Branson

This small but potent seed is dedicated
to each reader who strives to achieve their greatest
potential and to bring out the best from within.
Bloom to your highest.
Be all that you can be.
Fly!

My sincere gratitude to all my teachers in
the science of success and wealth. From the ones
who taught me by their example to the ones who
taught me by experience, and even to the ones who
taught me how not to be successful.
I bow to you all.

|Contents|

Author's Note

Have you ever wondered why you are not as successful as the person next to you? What are the traits of a successful person? And what sets the successful people of the world apart from others?

This has been a subject close to my heart from as far back as I can remember. Success is a powerful word for it encompasses so much. Success could come to you in terms of fame, wealth or social status. But a successful person is special; there is a certain something that makes him or her different.

Over many years of research and talking to people who have achieved phenomenal success all over the world, I have found that they are a breed apart—with strong beliefs in a set of common principles that they use daily to live their lives and to create vast amounts of abundance around themselves.

These secrets I have condensed and shared with you in this book: *The Little Manual of Success*. The qualities and characteristics of the super-achievers, and the principles and beliefs that motivate them, are all here.

Remember though that it all begins with you. You are the most important factor in your own life and in your own success. You alone will define what success means to you.

Use the knowledge in this book to create for yourself the life of your choice.

Vikas Malkani

|Chapter One|

Take Responsibility

Consult not your fears but your hopes and your dreams. Think not about your frustrations, but about your unfulfilled potential. Concern yourself not with what you tried and failed in, but with what it is still possible for you to do.

Pope John XXIII

It is so easy to point fingers and blame others. In fact, today, criticising, complaining and blaming have become almost fashionable. People seem to enjoy wallowing in self-pity, whining or commenting, "It is not fair." It seems as if they revel in being victims.

That is not the way to achieve success. We have to take responsibility for our actions and thoughts. We have to create a brave new world and realise that the onus for a better tomorrow lies with us. A verse that we all learnt when we were kids comes to mind, its simple message appropriate:

Because of the nail, the shoe was lost.
Because of the shoe, the horse was lost.
Because of the horse, the rider was lost.
Because of the rider, the battle was lost.
Because of the battle, the kingdom was lost.
And all because of a horseshoe nail.

Is the nail to blame? Who is to take responsibility for the lost kingdom? Is success possible for those who pass the buck?

I believe that *now* is the best time in the history of the planet to be alive. Never has there been more opportunity for the ordinary man or woman to have an impact on the world and create change in it. If you had been a woman or a minority member just 50 years ago, it would have been impossible even to pursue your interests beyond the boundaries society imposed on you. The wonderful inventions and technologies of today, the personal computer and the Internet, have empowered the individual.

Where it was once a capital-intensive world of steel mills and assembly lines, it has become a world of innovative ideas and personal vision.

To succeed in today's world, you do not need millions of dollars. All you need is imagination and courage. And the strength to own up to all that you do. In other words, all you need is your mind, and will power!

It is only when you give your consent to something that it becomes your reality

As Richard Bach puts it: "Within each of us lies the power of our consent to health and sickness, to riches and poverty, to freedom and to slavery. It is we who control these, and not another."

It is only when you give your consent to something that it becomes your reality. This is not to say that changing one's attitude is a simple matter. It is much easier, safer and comfortable to let the constant pull of mediocrity hold you back. Somehow, somewhere along the development of our own personalities, we have come to expect that we are owed something. We have adopted the mistaken notion that if the nation is experiencing an economic upswing, we deserve our share. This is an attitude that encourages weakness and takes away from the power of the individual; this is certainly not the stuff millionaires are made up of.

This kind of thinking adds up to a collective unwillingness to take responsibility for our own lives. When we fall short, instead of owning up and saying, "I was wrong," we point fingers anywhere but at ourselves. The governments, the nation, society in general, other people, or even God—all are innocent scapegoats for our inabilities and weaknesses. We have become masters in the blame game.

Every time you shun responsibility, you are actually trying to avoid failure. The concept of failing a few times in a noble pursuit, persevering, and then finally succeeding, has become quaint, almost old-fashioned, and is considered passé by most people. And on those increasingly rare occasions when we do act on an opportunity, or an idea, we tend to give it less than our best effort.

If you have a dream, there is no justification for exerting anything less than your total effort to make it happen. Nothing can justify not giving yourself fully to the vision or the dream of your life. Similarly, there is no justification for resorting to excuses when you fall on your face—whatever the reason may be.

Here is the first secret of millionaires, people who are successful in life: Learn to take responsibility for yourself and do it NOW!

Take your life in your own hands, whatever your life may be so far. Accept all parts of it, the good and the bad, as being *your* creation. For only when you accept responsibility for the whole, can you change a part of it.

★ If you have a dream, there is no justification for exerting anything less than your total effort to make it happen ★

Here are three suggestions for you to arrive at a state of responsibility for yourself and your life in totality:

1. Start living in the present tense. Stop dwelling on what happened yesterday. Do not think about what could or should or would have been. Concentrate on what you can do today and what tomorrow can offer.

2. Stop measuring yourself by the standards of others. Be authentic. You don't have a responsibility to be like anyone else. It is fine if you just be the best that you can be. No

matter what you achieve or how often you fail, you will never be the best or the worst. Your life journey is a relative experience. Accept the fact that each of your competitors has strengths and weaknesses. Start with what you have and grow from there.

3. Take action—any action. If you do nothing, nothing will change. If you do the same old stuff, you will end up with the same old results. The only way to change your situation is to take responsibility and try something different.

As we travel through life, we collect positive and negative baggage. This baggage comes in the shape of experiences, incidents and fateful meetings. If you are not careful, you can get so bogged down with negative baggage that it can wear away your confidence. It is up to you to take personal responsibility to decide what to hold on to and what is not worth carrying any further. You must decide where you want to keep your attention and your vision.

Keep in mind the ancient spiritual law, "Whatever you focus on, grows." You can choose to look at the sunshine in your life or the shadows. Just remember that whatever you put your attention on, will become your reality.

The choice of where we put our attention is with us. We decide on what we want and then we watch it getting manifested in our lives—for better or for worse.

We are responsible for every act of ours, as well as for every thought. We alone make the decisions and the onus of what happens as a result of those decisions lies with us.

★ Whatever you focus on, grows ★

Life helps those who help themselves. It's up to you. If you want to be somebody, if you want to be a success, you will always have to keep in mind that you are the only one who can make it happen.

Think big, think positive, and you are already on your way to success. How can failure come to someone who is ready to take on the world and accept that he or she alone is responsible for the good and the bad times? Keep your vision kingsize.

Success Secret 1

Take responsibility!

Millionaires know and accept their ability to create their life and their reality

| Chapter Two |

Believe in Yourself

Believe in yourself! Have faith in your abilities! Without a humble but reasonable confidence in your own powers you cannot be successful or happy.

Norman Vincent Peale

You have got to have faith in what you do. For if you do not believe in yourself, in your thoughts and deeds, no one else will. It is this belief that will help you in your path to success. Simply put, a millionaire is one who is confident of his or her actions, s/he is aware that success will come their way over time if they put in their best efforts and believe that they will always win.

From faith comes a reflective strength in your personal state of being. From faith comes a sense of destiny and purpose. More important than what religion you belong to, or what philosophy of life you follow, is your faith. Believe in yourself, listen to that inner voice as it guides you.

There are people who have accepted fully the truth that they are not going to live forever, and have made a choice based on this acceptance. They have therefore decided to live life fully in every moment. These are people who have learnt to live from the heart, rather than to dwell in the mind. They have made a choice to express, give and share their love, thereby holding nothing inside, and as a result remaining empty to receive. They have a life based on total faith, rather than on pure logic. These people have understood that faith is what your heart tells you is true even when your mind cannot prove it. They live by the truth that we are not human beings having a spiritual experience; rather, we are spiritual beings having a physical one.

Courage comes from having faith—faith in others, in ourselves, in our individual beliefs and in our dreams. Faith can be focussed on God, on the universe, on a mission, or on people. Having faith in people is a vital part of succeeding in life and, indeed, of being a part of the human race.

One way to find faith in others and in ourselves is to make a commitment to whatever you wish to achieve and then call on the universe or a higher power to help you to accomplish it. When you can depend on your faith, you know you are not alone in your challenge. You know the universe is with you and that, even in the darkest times, the higher power invariably hears you.

★ From faith comes a sense of destiny and purpose ★

I find great strength in believing in a higher power that I call God. My early family life nurtured within me a personal relationship with God that has given me great stability and faith in the face of occasional overwhelming fear. I speak with God in an open, honest manner about what is in my heart and on my mind. By doing this, I have felt a sense of peace and calm that is truly awesome in its power. From personal experience I can tell you that believing in a higher power has made me stronger and kept me stable even as the storms of life hit me.

If you wish to overcome your fears and find the courage to be who you really are, you have to believe you are worthy of achieving your goals. If you do not believe in yourself, you have little or no chance of being successful.

Here are some of the reasons why you are worth believing in:

1. Do you try in your day-to-day actions to be honest?
2. Do you try to be loyal?
3. Do you try to be friendly?
4. Do you try to be dependable?
5. Do you try to be fair?
6. Do you try to show concern for others' feelings?
7. Do you try to do the right things in the right way?
8. Do you try and contribute to the world around you through your mind, emotions and body?

People are fundamentally good. We prefer to do the right thing, but because of the pressures of everyday living, we sometimes lose sight of our basic values.

Even though our destination is clear, often we find ourselves straying from the chosen path for reasons we ourselves cannot identify or justify. Deep down, you are a great person. Once you believe this, your courage will begin to grow substantially. You will be ready to face the world—come what may. Armed with this belief in yourself, you will be able to overcome all obstacles. As Sri Paramahansa Yogananda said: "When my trials become very great, I first seek understanding in myself. I don't blame circumstances or try to correct anybody else. I go inside first. I try to clean the citadel of my soul to remove anything that obstructs the soul's all-powerful, all-wise expression. That is the successful way to live."

★ If you do not believe in yourself, you have little or no chance of being successful ★

How many of us spend time and effort visiting the citadel of our soul? How many of us are aware that it is there, deep down, that we can find the answers to life's complexities? It is there that our faith—in ourselves and in humanity—is born. And it is that faith that will undoubtedly lead us to success.

Success Secret 2

Believe in yourself!

Millionaires believe that they are special, and have something to contribute

| Chapter Three |

Be a Student of Life, for Life!

That is what learning is. You suddenly understand something you've understood all your life, but in a new way.

Doris Lessing

Life is a school and there are many lessons to be learnt here. Success in any area of life is not simply an activity but an understanding, too. The following seven laws of success are actually mental strategies that can be easily incorporated into our day-to-day actions. Try and include as many of them as you can in your own life, and in the work that you do. Use them and see the results.

But before I share these seven laws with you, I ask you to keep in mind what Confucius wisely said so many centuries ago: "Learning without thought is labour lost; thought without learning is perilous." Dwell on each law. Understand its nuances; meditate on each. These seven laws could well be your signposts to success.

Law 1: *Act as if you can*

You are capable of those things that you are capable of believing. Or, to put it another way, you should always act as if you *can*. With this right mental attitude, you can then find out the truth regarding your innate potential by living out the experience.

Life is a school and there are many lessons to be learnt here

Sadly, far too many of us do the opposite. We decide ahead of time that we cannot. We think we are too old, too young, too poor, too hopeless, not blessed with the right parents and so on. Such negative thinking limits performance. Turn the negative around, and suddenly the impossible becomes possible. When you believe and think, "I can," you activate your motivation, commitment, confidence and concentration, all of which relate directly to maximising achievement. On the other hand, if you think, "I cannot," you sabotage your chances of achieving your goals.

Experts agree that all of us have deep reservoirs of ability that we habitually neglect to use. We fail to make use of our talents because we are caught up in the absurd and impossible game of imitating others who, unfortunately, are not worthy of emulation. Since there is no one on earth just like you, how can you be inferior?

Men and women who have made the greatest contributions to humanity were often scorned by others. So do not be afraid if you are criticised—you are in good company. You are in the company of Noah, who was criticised for building a boat in the middle of the desert. You are in the company of Galileo, who was criticised for postulating that the earth revolved around the sun, and of Moses, who led a group of people from nowhere to somewhere for forty long years. You are walking the path blazed by Nelson Mandela, whose unquenchable thirst for freedom liberated a nation. You are with those who believed in themselves when the world did not believe in them. But, today, we cite them as examples for others to emulate.

Optimism means expecting the best, but self-confidence means feeling capable of handling the worst, if the worst happens. A successful person is confident that s/he can change lives, including their own.

Law 2: *Have the vision to realise that you will succeed*

The successful man or woman has a guiding vision, a dream, a sense of focus. The millionaire believes that it is his or her divine right to dream. He or she believes that the Almighty provides us with control over the power to shape our own thoughts and the privilege of placing them into any pattern of our choice. We alone weave our dreams in the intricate tapestry of life.

Each achiever says in his or her own unique way: "I am God's child and success and fulfilment is my right." As I have often said, we are not just human beings trying to make it in this world. We are spiritual beings going through a human experience on the way towards complete expression and fulfilment. In this belief lies the seed of greatness. It is this vision that underlines all our actions and thoughts. It is what makes us tick.

Law 3: *Be passionate about what you do*

Chiselled upon the tomb of an inept, disappointed Pharaoh in ancient Egypt is the epitaph: "Here lies a ruler who, with the best intentions, never carried out a single plan." The king just did not have the passion or the motivation to make his dreams come true.

Many of us go through life searching for breakthroughs. We would do better if we went through life backed with the power of a single aim, and persisted with patience to achieve it.

> ★ We alone weave our dreams in the intricate tapestry of life ★

Do not be lackadaisical about this. Passion is one of the most important ingredients in the recipe for success. "If you set yourself on fire," said the inimitable Don King, "the world will come to see you burn!" Ignite the fire within; move ahead with single-minded determination. And success will be yours.

Law 4: *Do not be afraid of making mistakes*

Life shrinks or expands in proportion to one's courage—this is a spiritual truth. Courage means the willingness to take risks, to accept challenges. Courage means you have the ability to stretch your comfort zone.

Men and women of courage do not worry about failure; they focus on the path to success. High-achievers accept setbacks on the path to success courageously, understanding that we cannot stretch our limits without encountering some rough moments along the way. It takes courage to stand firmly while others move back or give up in fear; it takes courage to forsake today for tomorrow; it takes courage to stake the known for the unknown; it takes courage to let the one bird in hand free for the two (or more) in the bush, and it takes great courage to stand alone and fight for what you want.

Law 5: *Be honest and open in all that you do*

Character is what you are in the dark. It is the way you behave when there is no one watching you or passing judgement on your deeds. Character is what you really are. In other words, character is your integrity, the values that determine who you are. The successful are always open and honest in all business transactions. Character is the one quality that cannot be acquired, only earned. Every thought that enters our mind, every word we utter, every deed we perform, makes its impression upon the innermost fibre of our being, and the result of these impressions is our character.

It has been anonymously written: "Fame is a vapour, popularity is an accident, and money takes wing. The only thing that endures is character." Nobody knows this better than the successful individual.

Law 6: *Work towards becoming the best*

Sometimes good is simply not enough. At a final interview with the president of a major corporation, a highly recommended young woman was asked two important questions: "Exactly what can you do for us?" and "What are your specialities?"

"I can do almost anything," the young lady replied.

"Well," said the president, rising to his feet, "I have no use for anyone who can do 'almost' anything. I'm looking for someone who can do one thing to perfection."

Passion is one of the most important ingredients in the recipe for success

Everywhere, there are men and women who are "almost" successful. You will find a man who is almost a lawyer but not quite; a woman who is almost a doctor but did not finish medical school. How many people have "almost" mastered a second language? The world is full of well-meaning efforts that end up as half-completed results. There is a great crowd of humanity who can "attempt or half-do" many things, but cannot do one thing to perfection. Competence is the difference between excellence and mediocrity. And all successful people are unwilling to settle for mediocrity.

Law 7: *Conquer yourself*

"The first and best victory," Plato wrote, "is for a man to conquer himself." Men and women search their entire lives looking for fame and fortune without attaining either. This is because they do not understand that the real source of wealth and achievement rests within their own minds and can only be released by the power of strict self-discipline. Discipline is indispensable to all leadership. It is the foundation of a man of determination, and determination and discipline guided by a vision pave the way for unimaginable wealth and success. Together, they make millionaires.

The mind that is properly disciplined and directed to a clear-cut objective cannot be defeated. An ancient Hindu proverb says, "There is nothing noble in being superior to some other man. True nobility is in being superior to your previous self."

If you want to manifest success in your life, carefully consider these four mental strategies, and make them a part of your life and work:

1. Be open and honest.

2. Question yourself repeatedly about those traits that you already possess and those in which you need to improve.

3. As you develop a vision and are confident about your abilities, work at improving your self-discipline.

4. Self-discipline will lead to even greater effectiveness in the areas of:
   a. Passion
   b. Courage

c. Character
d. Competence
e. Self-confidence

All successful people are unwilling to settle for mediocrity

Be sure to tap the spiritual force within. This comes from an understanding of the fact that you are a special and unique child of God; that you are an essential part of this universe.

In concluding this chapter, let me repeat these seven laws. Remember, these are the seven laws of millionaires—successful men and women who know what it takes to make them leaders in their chosen fields.

Law 1: Act as if you can
Law 2: Have the vision to realise that you will succeed
Law 3: Be passionate about what you do
Law 4: Do not be afraid of making mistakes
Law 5: Be honest and open in all that you do
Law 6: Work towards becoming the best
Law 7: Conquer yourself

Success Secret 3

Learn constantly!

Millionaires remain lifelong students and learn from their role models

|Chapter Four|

See It to Be It

The most important thing is that you see your goal in front of you. You always have to see it in front of you, because that will become the motivating force for you.

Arnold Schwarzenegger

When you are getting ready to take the first step into the unknown, visualise yourself succeeding, for that very thought will help you in building momentum. The truth of our existence is that our bodies go where our thoughts go. If you can visualise victory in your mind, you can achieve it. Your body will follow your mind; together, they will lead you to success.

The reasoning behind this is very simple. When you visualise yourself succeeding and think positively, you fuse your conscious and unconscious energies into a singular mission. This visualised courage has an emotional quality and almost feels like a surge of energy coursing through your body. This is the energy that is going to empower you and give you the strength to pursue your goal. A millionaire is one who has not only seen this goal, he or she is blessed with the vision to make it happen.

If your mind can conceive something and your heart can believe it, your body can achieve it. When you believe something, your body accepts it as your truth. Your brain produces the chemicals that are needed to keep you enthusiastic, energetic, strong and focussed. All your organs become allies; they have a common vision and it is their intent to make sure that it becomes a reality. What you can see is pretty much what you are going to get. Think positive, think like a winner, dream big dreams—and you are well equipped to script your success story. On the other hand, negative visualisation has an impact that is more than just mental. When you are overcome by negative thoughts, your mouth is dry and your hands tremble. If you laugh at all, it is a nervous laugh. You are actually an apology of what you could be, if only your thoughts were lofty, your vision sublime.

★ If your mind can conceive something and your heart can believe it, your body can achieve it ★

Here is a three-step visualisation process that will bring you closer to success:

1. Imagine experiencing the trappings of success. Picture yourself standing in the winner's circle, and hold tightly to the feeling of having arrived successfully. Imagine the smiles, the thanks, the congratulations, the applause and all the wonderful feelings that come your way once you have succeeded.

2. Visualise walking backwards one step at a time. Rewind your mental tape from victory to your current position.

What was required at each step? Build in your mind a wave of successes that smoothens out the bumps of fear from your current position to ultimate success.

3. Take the crucial initial step forward. With the feeling of success fuelling your motivational fire, move ahead to victory. Take action! The key to your journey is the feeling in your heart that you have already arrived before you have even started.

Remember, negative visualisation is not always instantaneous. It often simmers quietly over time and may take months, years and entire lifetimes to develop and grow. It is a silent killer for it saps us of all energy. It takes away from us the will to succeed. It is really what makes a loser. The subconscious mind speaks to us without us even being aware of its words. This chatter continues all the time and becomes our self-talk. This is what we begin to believe we are, or are not, capable of.

When you are not countering a negative fear, you are nurturing it. The more time and attention you give to your thoughts, the more they grow and become real for you. And if these negative thoughts are taking up your energy, guess what you are growing in your own mind?

The time you postpone dealing with your thoughts is the time you are allowing them to sink roots in your mind. Soon, even a tiny, totally irrational fear can grow into a raging one that can cripple you as effectively and completely as a set of steel handcuffs. Years of feeling that you are stupid, ugly or inept can stifle your ability to live life to its fullest. Your feeling of incompetency can become a raging monster within you.

Be alert to your negative thoughts, words and images. Keep a close inventory of them. When you feel a new negative stereotype come into being in the back of your mind, go after it, expose it, dissect it, familiarise yourself with it, and find out what gave rise to it in the first place. After that, replace it with the most positive and successful thought you can find. Albert Einstein once taught how to attempt at visualising the Fourth Dimension: "Take a point, stretch it into a line, curl it into a circle, twist it into a sphere, and punch through the sphere." In a similar manner, take your negative thoughts, understand and rationalise them, find out where they came from and where they are heading. And then just punch them out of your mind.

> What you can see is pretty much what you are going to get

If you can learn how to use your own subconscious mind, you will have a wonderful and strong ally at your side at all times, regardless of what life brings you. Here is how you can do it. Let us explore the seven steps that will activate the subconscious mind and take us to great heights. But before that, let us understand what the subconscious mind is; let us appreciate what it is capable of.

Deep down below the surface of our thoughts lies that powerful component of our mind that we call the subconscious. Our subconscious mind is the storehouse of our memory; it holds the impressions of our entire past.

Nothing can approach the powerful capabilities of the subconscious mind. But to be successful in any aspect of our life, we must make greater use of it. Unfortunately, most of us go through life without ever realising how to use this fountain of power. Only a small percentage of people discover the subconscious mind, understand it, and subsequently learn how to guide its hidden powers to achieve complete success.

When you know how to use the hidden power of your subconscious mind, you can attain riches beyond your wildest dreams. Your subconscious mind can activate your imagination and inspire you with new thoughts and fresh ideas. You can use this power to gain the financial prosperity that will offer you a new level of freedom to be whatever you want and do whatever you want. Your subconscious mind can also help you locate your true purpose in life and to determine what you are best suited to do so you may utilise your innate talents. Through this power, you'll be able to find the right position or vocation that will eventually lead you to fulfilment.

You can use your subconscious mind to rid yourself of frustration, anger and resentment. This hidden guide will help you solve your most pressing problems and lead you to make the right decision. You can also use its power to free yourself from fear, anxiety and worry forever. It will deactivate and defuse a failure attitude and replace it with a much more positive outlook.

As its name suggests, the subconscious mind is lying dormant within you, below your consciousness, just waiting to be placed into action. Your subconscious mind is unlimited, infinite and inexhaustible. It never rests; it keeps working every moment of your life. You need only to activate it and put its marvellous power to use.

★ The more time and attention you give to your thoughts, the more they grow and become real for you ★

One of the principles many achievers use is: Find a need and fill it. The same principle applies to your subconscious mind. You must give it a goal to reach, an objective to achieve, before it will go into action. Your subconscious mind operates best in a climate of faith and acceptance, confidently expecting that your problems will be solved and obstacles removed.

Here is a seven-step procedure that will unleash the power of the subconscious mind:

1. Realise that your goals can be achieved—this is the mental state that intensifies thought and causes the subconscious mind to function at its best.

2. Know exactly what it is you want to accomplish. Be specific about the goal you want to reach, the objective you want to attain.

3. Believe in your heart that your subconscious mind will invariably deliver the answer you want or need.

4. Separate facts from opinions. Do your homework thoroughly and gather all available matter on the subject.

5. Feed these facts into your subconscious mind with an earnest request for an answer.

6. Relax. Watch diligently and wait patiently for the right answer or the appropriate solution. Trust that it will come in the due course of time.

7. Take immediate action when the answer arrives. The first six steps are of extreme importance but they will be wasted if you do not rise to the occasion. If you fail to act, your subconscious mind will reach the conclusion that you are not serious about your requests for help.

Scientific breakthroughs, great musical compositions, inspiring books and all other innovative ideas for original accomplishment are born within the subconscious mind. It is the singular source of all inspiration and motivation; it brings into being the excitement that rushes over you when confronted

with a ne ... ibility. It is also
the so ... ion and
flash

V ... t it works
... nd is calm.
... have to retreat-
... r mind where
... ce. Program your
... ordingly. You can
... rself to be brave and confident. Or you can
... yourself to despair. Try this as a simple exercise.
... yourself for fear. Drum up some negative thoughts.
... ompetent," "scared to death," "I'll never make it," "It's
... ess." You will now feel that your body and mind has been
... itioned for failure. If you feel this is working on you, always
... member that the opposite effect can be created by repeating
words such as "tranquillity" and "serenity".

When you know how to use the hidden power of your subconscious mind, you can attain riches beyond your wildest dreams

Take a moment to reflect on the person you were before you picked up this book. On which side of the divide between a positive outlook and sheer negativity did your thoughts fall? Did you approach your life's journey with positive thoughts that generate confidence, hope and courage? Or did you see only the dark side and, for the sake of avoiding disappointment, expect only the worst? Think about the positive and negative components of your life as it is. What feeds your personality? Do you dwell on fears, insecurities, stereotypes, prejudices and the negative experiences of the past? Or are the thoughts that define you ones that are aimed at doing, challenging, risking and achieving? Are you someone who clings to security, or do you have the courage to risk insecurity?

Here is something you should remember—to become successful, you have to train yourself to become comfortable with insecurity! Great are those who have the ability to walk out of their defined space and think out of the box. Let there be no boundaries in your mind. As Robert Green Ingersoll said, "Surely there is grandeur in knowing that in the realm of thought, at least, you are without a chain; that you have the right to explore all heights and depth; that there are no walls nor fences, nor prohibited places, nor sacred corners in all the vast expanse of thought." Take wing, let your thoughts be big and profound. And then go make them happen.

Fear is the biggest obstacle to visualisation; it is also the single greatest obstacle to success. For some, fear blocks the path to the achiever's circle. For others, it creates total paralysis. No one enslaved by fear is rich, either materially or spiritually. It is fear that robs us of our happiness and freedom, our peace of mind. The only positive aspect regarding the emotion of fear is that it is learned and, consequently, it can be un-learned.

There are four basic fears that constrain our life—the fear of death, of poverty, of change and uncertainty and of failure.

They make us forget that fear is controlled, not overcome. The expression of fear denies men and women the use of the true power of thought. Each of us, to some degree, suffers from one or more of these four fears; some people suffer from all of them. The courageous are not men and women who have yet to experience the paralysing emotions of fear. Courageous people act in spite of their fears.

When you face your fears and move towards them, they diminish and recede. But when you back away from the circumstance or person that you fear, the powers of fear grow until they can actually dominate your life. You must drive out these negative influences before the positive power of courage can overtake your inhibitions. Probe deeply into your subconscious and be sure that none of these four deadly fears resides within your mind.

> To become successful, you have to train yourself to become comfortable with insecurity

"I'm not afraid of storms, for I'm learning how to sail my ship," said Louisa May Alcott. Look fear in the face and get ready to sail your ship.

Fear of Death

It is startling to discover how many people just give in to the idea of death and begin to make all sorts of preparations for death, even at a time when they should be enjoying the fullness of life. I believe death is to be celebrated, not feared. Life is not simply a journey between two points on an endless highway. Life is eternal and we are alive in eternity *now*. Death has no place in the fullness of life and the individual who embraces the idea of life fully cannot die.

What we think of as death is simply the movement of the soul from one vessel of experience of life into another. Instead of learning how to die, we should simply be spending our time learning how to live fully.

It may be difficult for most people to interpret death as being anything but an unavoidable tragedy, but this limited view can be broadened by understanding the great plan of the universe: You and I are perfect now—created perfectly—and we are one with our Creator.

The will of God is the ceaseless longing of the spirit in you to completely fulfil your potential. It is God seeking to express Himself as you—as inner joy, as radiant health, as eternal youth, as freedom from limitation and as unlimited success.

It is only when we rise up in the realisation of our divine nature of immortality and omnipotence that we can free ourselves from the terrible fear of death.

There is this ancient story of an old sage sitting beneath a tree in Egypt as the spirit of the plague went by.

"Whither goest thou?" the wise man asked. "I go to Cairo, where I shall slay one hundred Egyptians," was the reply.

Three months later, the spirit of the plague again passed the old sage on its journey.

"You said you would slay one hundred in Cairo, but travellers tell me you slew ten thousand," said the wise man in disbelief.

To which the spirit of the plague replied, "I slew but one hundred. Fear slew the rest!"

No one enslaved by fear is rich, either materially or spiritually

As we learn to be at home in the spiritual and mental world and accept that death is an essential part of life and may visit anytime, all our fears lessen. With the easing of fear comes an easing of the effects of fear. None of us have ever been promised a life free of pain or disappointment. In fact, what we have been promised is that even though pain and trouble are an inherent part of our physical life, we need not be alone in our pain. We can draw upon a source outside ourselves for strength and courage.

The universe does not create our suffering, we do by the way we use our mind. Our attitude determines our perspective. Whether something is an opportunity or a crisis depends not on the thing itself, but rather on the eyes with which we see that thing.

Fear of Poverty

Nothing brings humanity so much struggle and humiliation as poverty. I define poverty not as a shortage of money or wealth but rather a mindset that always feels the lack in life rather than the abundance. A poverty mindset is insecure and thus goes on to create for itself a physical reality that resonates its thoughts.

It is hard to live a complete or successful life unless one feels rich—materially or spiritually. No one can rise to his or her full potential in talent or soul development unless s/he possesses an 'abundance' consciousness. Wealth and prosperity begin within us long before they become apparent in our physical and material world, and it all begins in the arena of our thoughts—the mind.

Everything that lives has a right to the free and unrestricted use of all things that may be necessary to fulfil its highest mental, physical and spiritual development—in other words, your right to be rich!

However, the fear of poverty circulates around the idea that too many people believe they have no value to bring to the world. These individuals are very often infected with the negative consciousness of personal need rather than inspired by the positive consciousness of personal value. As a result, there appear to be more people feeling needy than those who feel valuable.

This fear paralyses the gift of imagination, destroys self-reliance, circumvents enthusiasm and ambition, and breeds the habit of negative expectation. Instead of concentrating on why a particular idea might work, the individual discovers all the reasons why a given plan or concept will not work and acts accordingly.

The Creator of our universe and everything in it views you and me as pure value or unlimited potential. In other words, you are too valuable to be poor; you are too valuable to be a downtrodden human being; you are too valuable to be lifeless or hopeless; you are too valuable to be meaningless. We live in a world that demands value and, in turn, rewards value with money. Once you realise how valuable you are and how much you have going for you, the smiles will return, the sun will break out of the clouds, wealth will find its way to your door, and you will finally be able to live in the manner congruent with your highest potential and dreams.

☆ Instead of learning how to die, we should simply be spending our time learning how to live fully ☆

Fear of Change and Uncertainty

Many would-be achievers are held back by the prospect of giving up a steady pay cheque or facing the unknown. But, to be creative, to venture forward, to succeed, one must be willing to lose what one has—to embrace uncertainty, to replace security with insecurity.

To find true happiness, to be fulfilled, to be at peace with yourself and others, you must learn to take risks.

The path to success in life is paved with the virtue of courage, taking action, and possessing the flexibility to change until you have reached your objective. If you fear change, you will never arrive at a state of excellence.

Those who have become successful in this world have learnt to step out boldly into the unfamiliar world and make it familiar. They have learnt to become familiar with the unfamiliar, comfortable with the uncomfortable. They are on the highway to success simply because they have chosen to tread the unknown path. Their life is an adventure, a world full of challenges and paved by risks. It is lots of fun because they choose to view it like that. They are the winners for they are the ones who are not fazed by change and uncertainty, come what may.

Fear of Failure

The fear of failure is the major cause of stress and negativity. It is also the biggest reason why most people never fulfil their dreams. Simply put, failure is nothing more than a few errors in judgement repeated every day. Keep this in mind and you will achieve all that you can conceive in your mind. You will never fail; you will simply produce results. High-achieving men and women are not people who never fail; they are people who try something and if it does not give them what they want, they simply dismiss it as a learning experience. They then go on to use what they have learned and try something else.

They don't let the setbacks of life hold them down. They don't allow failures to become their reality. They learn from them and continue to move forward in an improved manner.

Failures help the rich become rich, the successful become successful. This is because if and when failure does come, the truly positive people use it like a friend and not an adversary who is out to get them.

A poverty mindset is insecure and thus goes on to create for itself a physical reality that resonates its thoughts

There is this Swedish proverb that states that worry gives a small thing a big shadow. If we think of something as a big deal, it becomes just that. Then it will rear its big fat head and scare the life out of us.

We fail because we are too scared to accept the fact that fear is just a stepping stone to success. History has taught us that many brave men and women have conquered tough obstacles; they have fought their way through anguish and defeat to great personal triumph.

"Failure is, in a sense, the highway to success," noted William Keats, a nineteenth century essayist, "in as much as every discovery of what is false leads us to seek earnestly after what is true, and every fresh experience points out some form of error which we shall afterwards carefully avoid."

The one critical success question that removes all failure from your life is: "What can I do better next time?"

If you address this question, you ensure that you will redouble your efforts and try, try, try again, until you reach your objective. Remember the plucky spider that just went on weaving? This little insect was an inspiration for a fallen king; it could well be a lesson for all of us.

You must realise that all external events lack any emotional component in their make-up. All external events are inherently neutral until you mentally respond and assign an emotional context to them. With this realisation, you will understand that nearly all fears are imaginary. They are a product of your mind and do not exist in reality. The key to eliminating unnecessary fears from your life is to create and hold on firmly to positive images and thoughts. Your fear is real only to the extent that you allow your mind to create it, and then allow your body to feel it.

Remember, the universe never consults your past to determine your future. To fight with fear and to achieve victory over it, you have to increase the reservoir of courage within you. Courage comes from the same place that fear comes from—

your mind. It is up to you which one you want to feed and allow to grow.

Anyone can develop the quality of courage, but it takes a lot of effort and daily practice.

Try these seven steps to increase your courage quotient:

★ The path to success in life is paved with the virtue of courage, taking action, and possessing the flexibility to change until you have reached your objective ★

Step 1: *Bring out your special-ness*

Realise that you are one of a kind.

Develop your originality, resourcefulness and the ability to assert your individuality. Become a self-starter, an independent thinker who is able to carry out your own plans. Your each act of courage is an option exercised that helps to build a reservoir of energy and faith in your ability to achieve.

The more challenges you face, the more you can conquer. And the more you conquer, the more special you will be.

Step 2: *Stop using the word 'failure'*

Many achievers would like to see the word 'failure' stricken from the dictionary. For them, there is no failure, only feedback. Their mistakes are their lessons. Live and learn is their credo. The successful teach you that you should not dwell on your mistakes or setbacks, but instead learn from them and then move on.

Become a sponge for new information and develop knowledge in your chosen field of endeavour. Put this knowledge into action. Commit yourself to reaching your objectives and let nothing deter you. There is no such thing as failure. You never fail, you simply produce results. Failure cannot happen in your life without your permission.

Step 3: *Be prepared to succeed*

Help to insulate yourself to succeed by mapping a plan and then follow through with appropriate action, regardless of the circumstances.

Plan your work and work your plan is the way the achievers of this world approach action. As they take one step, they also remain open to changes they may have to incorporate in the plan they have already made. In other words, even though they work to a plan, they do understand that the plan is a flexible one and will constantly need close attention and further improvement.

It will be necessary to adapt your plan to shifting conditions or new requirements. But keep your eyes on your goal. With this strategy, you will not only achieve your goals but also find yourself strengthened in the process.

Step 4: *Do not take failure personally*

Those who have experienced a failure often tend to view themselves and their failure as one and the same thing.

This is not an empowering way of moving into the future.

> ★ Failures help the rich become rich ★

You and your failure are not identical, and you must learn to view your past circumstances separately. When things go sour, do not label yourself a loser. A failure to produce the desired result does not in any way mean you have failed, it only means that the path of action needs to be modified somewhat and improved. The language you use to describe yourself can become a powerful reality, so be careful what words you use when you talk to yourself.

Shakespeare wrote, "Our doubts are traitors, and make us lose the good we often might win by fearing to attempt." Drive the doubts out as you develop the attitude that expresses courage, and never personalise your failure.

Step 5: *Learn to say, "I can!"*

Affirm to yourself with energy and conviction, "I can do it! I can do it!" This affirmation short-circuits and cancels out the feeling of "I can't! I can't!" Use your specific fear as a challenge and instead of backing away from it or avoiding it, confront it and face it head-on. Walk towards your fear, not away from it.

Step 6: *Know that you'll never walk alone*

Spiritual understanding gives you the strength and stamina to stand up, challenge and change each negative thought and feeling into a positive one.

One of the most consoling and truest assurances given to us is found in the Bible: "Fear not, for I am with you always."

This thought is echoed in other even more ancient scriptures from different parts of the world, such as the Bhagavad Gita from India where Lord Krishna says, "He who sees Me everywhere and sees all in Me, does not let Me perish and nor do I let him perish." The feeling of having God or a higher power near you at all times is truly comforting.

Keep this truth in your heart as you walk the path to success: "God is within me and strengthens me to follow the path to my dreams. I am a creator of my own life and destiny, and I can choose to create a life of my choice." You will then never walk alone.

Step 7: *Remain centred and meditate*

Still your mind and you will be able to see far into your own future and the actions that will get you there. It is when your thoughts are centred, when you look deep within in silence and solitude, that you are able to connect with the highest power. It is this power—God—that will help you reach your fullest potential and actualise your dreams.

Meditation, spending quiet time with yourself, is a sure way of success. However busy you are, this is one activity that is essential for your growth, both personal and professional. So if you are not in the habit of meditating, start *now*. Spend twenty minutes at the beginning of every day in silence. Sit quietly and focus on your objectives, not your obstacles. During meditation, your fears will disappear. Tap into the energy that is concentrated in the spaces between your thoughts. It is in the stillness that exists there that you will find the way to overcome your fears. Live in the present—it is indeed the best way to prepare for a future event.

Keep these proven action steps for courage in mind. When you practise these steps, you will never surrender to the darkness of fear again. You will discover that success is simply a matter of affirming positive expectations and moving forward. The world always stands aside for the courageous soul. So think of yourself as a brave person who is ready to face all obstacles and overcome all fears; believe in this. Visualise yourself reaching out for great heights. You will surely reach there.

★ Remember, the universe never consults your past to determine your future ★

Success Secret 4

Challenge fear!

Millionaires train themselves to be comfortable with risk

|Chapter Five|

Reject Mediocrity

Some people dream of success...while others wake up and work hard at it.

Anonymous

Successful people are those who have made a clear choice not to settle for mediocrity in their lives. They are aware of the fact that the majority of this world seems to have chosen a life of comfort and security; folks who never push their comfort zone to try and arrive at the optimisation of their own potential.

On the other side of the spectrum are the achievers—those who strive to reach a state of excellence and will not stop till they have left the world of mediocrity far behind.

There are some who are almost happy being mediocre. At times it appears there is a conspiracy out there to encourage mediocrity. As Robert Louis Stevenson said, "Most of our pocket wisdom is conceived for the use of mediocre people, to discourage them from ambitious attempts, and generally console them in their mediocrity."

Yet the mediocre are never recognised or rewarded by society, only the exceptional are. And the goal of the achievers is to achieve what others have not.

There are six obstacles to excellence that the achievers seek to overcome in their quest to soar far above the rest of mankind. But before you read them, it may not be a bad idea to keep Norman Vincent Peale's words in mind: "Stand up to your obstacles and do something about them. You will find that they haven't half the strength you think they have."

> ★ Successful people are those who have made a clear choice not to settle for mediocrity in their lives ★

Obstacle 1: *Being conditioned for mediocrity*

The successful understand that society conditions you for mediocrity right from your early days.

A study was conducted at a university in which rats received electric shocks every time they tried to take food from a tray. They soon completely stopped approaching the food tray because of their fear of these electric shocks.

Then the electricity was turned off and an even more scintillating and desirable meal was placed on the tray, but the rats still did not approach it. As time went on, the rats chose to starve to death rather than take the risk of approaching the tray. Can you imagine being so conditioned by past events that you would prefer starvation and death rather than confront the possibility of encountering what you fear? This study proved that our past continues to define our future until we decide otherwise.

Two more stories bring across the power of conditioning very strongly. The first is about fleas; the second is about elephants. If you place fleas in a shallow container, they quickly jump out. However, if you put a lid on that container for just a fixed period, they will jump like crazy at first, but they will soon give up their quest for freedom because every time they jump, they hit the lid that keeps them in. When the lid is then removed, instead of instantly jumping out, they will never attempt to leave the container again.

Like the rats, these fleas have become conditioned by past limitations and, therefore, accept that those limitations will continue to exist in the future.

An elephant has a big brain and is infinitely smarter than a flea or a rat. And yet circuses train baby elephants by tying them daily to a pole planted securely in the ground. As a baby, the elephant very quickly learned that when he felt a tug of the rope on his neck, he could not go any further. By the time he became an adult, he could be tied to a small pole that he could easily rip right out of the ground, but he did not even try because he had been conditioned to believe that when that rope is around his neck and he encounters the little 'tug', he must stop.

Like the rats, fleas and elephants, we were conditioned by our teachers, coaches, fellow students and even our parents to believe that we were average or ordinary kids, capable of accomplishing average achievements. We were always told to do what the others do. Society has taught us to be the same as the masses, to fit in, never to be different. We were never conditioned to be excellent, to reach for something that others had never dared to attempt. And even though our conditioning was totally unintentional on the part of those who conditioned us, it was and still is devastatingly powerful.

By the time most of us graduated from school, we had been fully conditioned for mediocrity. From that point on, we have had a nearly unchangeable tendency to accept mediocrity as the best we can do in nearly every area of our lives.

We accept marriages and relationships that are just 'okay' rather than strive to make them great. We do just what is expected of us in our jobs rather than try to break all previous records and do something different.

★ Our past continues to define our future until we decide otherwise ★

We do not attempt to take risks and convert our ideas into businesses because we truly believe that we are not capable of overcoming great risks and achieving extraordinary success.

We let dreams be dreams; we never convert them into reality.

This conditioning for mediocrity, right from our early days, has had terrible consequences. Many marriages have ended in divorce or exist unfulfilled because a couple did not have the vision to turn a mediocre or bad marriage into a truly rewarding one. Similarly, many people have ended up in a dissatisfying career because they believed it was the best in the light of their abilities, background or circumstances.

Most of us settle for less than the best because we are afraid to let go of the mediocre that is already in our hands.

This chain of being conditioned for mediocrity is truly devastating as it keeps you anchored to your base station with no hope of ever heading off into the unknown and achieving the summit of the mountain of your dreams.

This conditioning for safety and security keeps the ship of our lives anchored in a safe harbour rather than allow it to sail in the uncharted oceans. It makes a complete mockery of the age-old adage: "Nothing ventured, nothing gained."

So the question now becomes, "How can you cut this devastating chain and keep cutting it every time it appears in your life?"

The great news is that it is a lot easier than you think. All it takes is a conscious awakening to a reality that has long been hidden from you, a corresponding adjustment of your attitude, and setting aside a few minutes a week to engage in one of the most powerful activities you will ever take part in.

We need to simply de-condition ourselves. Like Roger Bannister, who broke the four-minute mark for a one-mile run at a time when it was considered physically impossible for an athlete to run a mile under four minutes. He managed this feat because he *believed* he could achieve it.

The first step in cutting this binding chain of mediocrity is an awakening. I am not referring to a spiritual event but simply waking up to the fact that you, too, have been conditioned for mediocrity.

Most of us settle for less than the best because we are afraid to let go of the mediocre that is already in our hands

The next step is even more important; to believe that even though you've been conditioned for mediocrity, you were designed and created for extraordinary achievements. In fact, God created you for extraordinary, awesome achievements—in all areas of your life.

An extraordinary achievement is one that brings a huge amount of benefit or fulfilment to us or to others. Two people who have a relationship that truly meets the other's deepest emotional needs have achieved an extraordinary relationship.

Parents who raise children who are truly motivated by their love of others, who have great qualities such as loyalty, courage, dependability and trustworthiness, are extraordinary parents.

All of this is to say that the true measure of your achievement is the amount of fulfilment you are able to bring to others and to yourself.

Keep in mind that we can accomplish extraordinary achievements in every area of life that is important to us. We do not have to sacrifice success in one to achieve it in another. We have to adopt a holistic attitude; there is no need to compartmentalise your life.

Now that you have been awakened to the fact that you are indeed capable of achieving your dreams, of achieving extraordinary things in every important area of your life, you need to make a definite attitude adjustment. If you can adopt this attitude and commit yourself to exploring and pursuing all the incredible opportunities that await you, the knowledge revealed here would empower you to achieve things you have not yet dared to dream.

This means that your past levels of achievement will not determine or limit your future level of achievement.

Here are three things for you to remember at all times:

1. You have been conditioned for mediocrity by false standards of measure, given and set by others for you—grades, popularity, athletic abilities, levels of income and amount of material possessions. These are not the true

measures by which you should judge yourself.

★ Begin by knowing that you have already arrived ★

2. You were designed and created to accomplish extraordinary things in every area of life that is important to you. You must realise that your past conditioning has anchored you to the base station, and acknowledge that such programming need not keep you anchored.

3. You must adopt the attitude of one who has been given the greatest computer in the universe and become committed to using it to achieve your dreams and to help others achieve theirs.

In other words, you must become like Jonathan Livingston Seagull who dared to rise above the mediocre and fly. A seagull who is bored with life, he pushes himself, learning everything he can about flying, until his unwillingness to conform results in his expulsion from his flock. One day, Jonathan is met by two seagulls who take him to a "higher plane of existence", where he meets other gulls who love to fly. Jonathan befriends a wise gull, Chiang, who teaches him the secret to successful living: "Begin by knowing that you have already arrived."

Obstacle 2: *Fearing to fail*

Of the many chains that keep people bound to their base stations and prevent them from achieving their dreams, the fear of failure is the strongest and hardest to overcome. It is a chain that begins to form and take hold of you in childhood and is usually fully developed and firmly anchored by the time you graduate from high school. It not only prevents you from achieving your dreams, it can be so oppressive and destructive that it can cause you to willingly set aside your dreams before you make the slightest attempt to achieve them. In fact, it often trains you to stop dreaming altogether.

The fear of failure literally stunts your emotional growth and convinces you to accept mediocrity in nearly every important aspect of life. Your vision, your hope and consequently your achievements are suppressed and all but destroyed by this merciless tyrant. And here is the surprising part—many of you have lived with your fear of failure for so long that it has moved into your subconscious.

Thus, most of the time you are not even aware of its presence and yet it exerts its moment-by-moment influence on every aspect of your personality and decision-making process.

Conscious or subconscious fear of failure cuts short your ability to achieve your dreams. The fear of failure is highly contagious, and is unwittingly passed from generation to generation.

For those who are parents, here is the scariest part of all. As long as your visions, hopes and achievements are disfigured and impaired by your fear of failure, you will unintentionally limit and destroy the visions, hopes and achievements of your children. This debilitating fear and its consequences are extremely contagious. Therefore, you must sever this chain, if not for your sake then for the sake of your children and everyone else you really love. Your goal must be to break its relentless grip and sever its hold in such a way that it will never seriously restrict you again.

Then there is the other kind of fear, a bad fear, and that is the fear of your enemy. This fear causes you to focus on the very things you should not fear. It brings with it devastating consequences that can create emotional paralysis, even death. For some people, this fear results in terrible phobias that make them virtual prisoners of their fears. For most, however, bad fear is subtler; yet its consequences are no less damning. It literally stops you from doing a lot of very good things.

★ Conscious or subconscious fear of failure cuts short your ability to achieve your dreams ★

On the other side, however, is the good fear, which teaches you your natural limits from your childhood. It taught you not to touch a hot stove (a second time). It taught you not to stay underwater too long, or jump off something that was too high. This good fear has taught most of us to obey those in authority and stay within the boundaries of the law. The good fear is a natural positive factor in our lives that brings with it several positive outcomes. So the question is, how can we distinguish between the good fear and the bad fear?

The good fear usually focusses on the long-term consequences of doing that which is right and good, while the bad fear usually focusses on short-term consequences. For example, a bad fear tells me not to ask questions because I might look stupid to my peers and superiors. A good fear, on the other hand, tells me if I do not ask these questions, I may not learn, and therefore will not be able to succeed. Thus the source of a bad fear tends to be the desire for immediate gratification or the fear of short-term or immediate loss.

Now that we can begin to distinguish a good fear from a bad fear, the question becomes, how do we detect a bad fear when it is more subtle than obvious, and once it is detected, how can we diffuse or defeat it?

How to Detect Subtle Fears

What do you really want? If you could accomplish anything you desire—in a relationship, a job, a career, or a business—what would it be?

This is the first question that can help you to determine the subtle fears that divert your path from extraordinary achievement to mediocre or ordinary achievements. Once you clearly define what you want, make a list of the obstacles that keep you from achieving it.

Once you have defined the obstacles, ask what is keeping you from confronting or overcoming them. This is where your fears will usually be uncovered.

Examples of Detecting Fears

Desire	Obstacle	Fear of Confrontation
Great marriage	Husband does not care about my feelings	He will get mad, criticise, or reject me and my concerns
More fulfilling job	Not qualified for better job	May fail to get qualified and lose all hope. May lose current job in the process
Have my own business	Not enough money for start-up	May be turned down for loan or fail to repay the one I get; may lose everything I have

For example, perhaps your answer to the question, "What do you really want in your marriage?" might be, "To have a relationship where my deepest emotional needs are consistently fulfilled." Your next question is, "What are the obstacles to achieving that kind of marriage?" Your answer may be, "My spouse does not know how to meet my deepest needs or, for that matter, does not care."

Now comes the moment of truth—identifying your subtle fears with the critical question, "What keeps me from confronting or overcoming this obstacle?"

It may be your fear of being rejected or criticised if you were to talk about it with your spouse. It may be your fear of discovering that he or she cares even less about your needs than you thought. It may be a fear of not being able to adequately communicate how you really feel. Whatever your subtle fears in any given area may be, the first step to overcoming them is to clearly identify and define them. Once you identify a fear, the next step is to diffuse and defeat it.

How to Diffuse Fears

Once you have detected a fear that has subtly or overtly guided your behaviour or caused you to accept mediocrity in place of the extraordinary, it becomes fairly easy to diffuse or defeat it.

When you diffuse a fear, it becomes like a diffused bomb—totally impotent and powerless to affect or harm you in any way. And once you have diffused it, you defeat it by simply moving forward as if it did not exist. The first step is to see that fear in its true perspective. Often you have magnified your fears way beyond their real stature. You have given them more importance than they merit.

Put fear into its true perspective by asking three questions:

1. What is the worst that can happen if that which I fear came upon me?

2. What is more likely to happen if that fear were to be actually realised?

3. What is the best outcome possible for me and for others if I acted contrary to or in spite of my fear?

The chart below shows how to use this exercise to diffuse the fears from an example in the previous chart:

Putting Fears into Perspective

Fear	Worst Case	Likely Case	Best Case
He will get mad, criticise, or reject me	Another disappointment; things will stay the same	He will not get that mad, and maybe he will hear me, and things will improve	He will understand what I am saying and feeling, and things will get a whole lot better

You will not necessarily eliminate a fear when you take it through this exercise, but you will put it into proper perspective so you can accurately weigh the risks versus the benefits. That in itself will relieve the stress that builds up when you bury your fears and hide from them. That in itself will help you grow.

This exercise will also uncover some of your weaknesses, which you can then focus on and strengthen.

Understanding Failure

The primary goal is not to eliminate every bad fear in your life (although that would be wonderful). Rather, the goal is to equip yourself with a means of defeating a particular type of fear that seems to invade every area of life and often severely limits your level of achievement—namely, your fear of failure.

The first step in achieving this goal is to understand the component parts—fear and failure. While fear is an emotion, failure is an event. And most times, the fear of failure even keeps you from trying to succeed. It keeps you from taking action, which is the most important component in the journey to your own success.

Here is how I define failure: Failure is an event in which you did not achieve your desired outcome.

But more important than the definition is the role failure plays in your life.

Failure's Role

Any failure you experience can be one of these two options:

1. A great teacher, you could even call it a powerful mentor, to your future success.

2. A tyrannical dictator that can drastically limit or even destroy all hopes of future success.

Is this good news or bad news? In fact, I believe it is great news because the role failure takes in each of your lives is your choice. Its role is never forced upon you. You can choose to assign it the role of a teacher and a mentor to your future success or you can assign it the role of a dictator that drastically limits or even destroys your future success.

> The role failure takes in each of your lives is your choice

Remember, there is no middle ground. It will be either one or the other!

The best way to avoid failure is to avoid risk. And the way to avoid risk is to attempt to achieve only that which you are positively sure you are able to achieve. If you operate like this, you set subconscious or conscious goals that are mediocre at best.

The goals that you set are what you achieve; thus mediocrity is what you get—in relationships, in jobs and careers, and in other areas of life where the pain of past failures dictates your goals. In this manner, the fear of failure takes its unrelenting hold on your mind and emotions and becomes the single greatest limiting force in your life.

You can eliminate this fear easily. You must first choose to assign all past and future failures to the role of being your teachers and mentors. You can do this by simply revisiting them after the initial pain has subsided and learning all you can from them. You not only try on your own to discover all the reasons behind your failures, but you seek the advice of others, asking them to help you discover the reasons why you had failed.

You will be amazed at all you will learn. If you write down what you learn and review it before you attempt your next goal in that area, your chances of success increase dramatically. On the other hand, if you do not revisit your failures, learn from them, write down what you have learned and review it, you will repeat the same mistakes over and over again.

Here is a three-step exercise towards detecting subtle fears, the fears that form the major roadblocks in your journey to success:

1. Take any area of your life (your career, your marriage or any other relationship, a hobby, finances and so on) and write down the answer to this question: If you could have anything you want to happen in that area, what would it be?

2. List any or all of the obstacles that prevent you from seeing that wish fulfilled.

3. Now list any fears that keep you from confronting that obstacle and trying to overcome it.

And now let us move on towards diffusing and defeating bad fears.

Take any of the fears you have listed above and answer the following three questions:

★ The goals that you set are what you achieve ★

1. What is the worst that can happen if that which I fear came upon me?

2. What is more likely to happen if that fear is realised?

3. What is the best possible outcome for me and others if the fear is not realised and I overcome the obstacle?

Obstacle 3: *Avoiding criticism*

Your conscious or subconscious efforts to avoid criticism sabotage you before you even attempt to achieve your dreams.

"I told you so!" "I can't believe you did that!" "What were you thinking about?" "You always do that!" "You never do that!" "Don't be ridiculous!" "Are you crazy?" "I knew that would happen!" "Why don't you listen to me!" and "Don't be so sensitive!" are just some of the rejoinders that you may encounter in your journey towards excellence. Receiving criticism is one of the hardest experiences you have to deal with on a daily basis, and yet giving criticism is as natural and easy as breathing.

Can you remember anything you were criticised for when you were growing up? What were some of the criticisms you received from your teachers, friends, parents, brothers or sisters, girlfriends or boyfriends? Now try to remember criticisms you have received during the past thirty days. Do any come to your mind?

Chances are that the criticisms you received are a lot easier to remember than the ones you handed out. Why?

The answer is that criticism hurts you far more deeply than you think it does. It hurts so deeply that your brain never lets go of it, even decades after you stopped thinking about it. In fact, criticism is so distasteful, disheartening and painful, that you constantly adjust your behaviour, not to achieve what is in your best interest and the best interest of others, but rather simply to avoid being criticised.

The fear of criticism causes people to withdraw from relationships that might otherwise be a source of tremendous joy. It causes them to stop doing or saying things that could help them and others. For example, you do not begin an exercise programme because, if you quit, someone will say, "I knew you wouldn't stick with it."

Or, you do not voice your opinion on how to improve a relationship or a project because someone might just say, "Don't be ridiculous" or "That will never work."

But there is a way that enables one to completely overcome the negative impact of anyone's criticism and completely defeat any negative consequences it might have in your life. There exists a way that can liberate you from your self-imposed restraints and enable you to be all that you really are and achieve what you are truly capable of achieving.

The only way to defeat the negative impact of criticism is to learn the right way to deal with it

It is quite simple—the way to defeat the negative impact of criticism, and to stop avoiding it, is to risk facing it. Once you look at it in the face, it fails to appear formidable.

The only way to defeat the negative impact of criticism is to learn the right way to deal with it. And there is only one right way to deal with criticism. Realise that any criticism you receive can be your best ally or your worst enemy, depending upon three things—its source, its accuracy and your response to it.

And whether it becomes your deadly enemy or your supportive ally is *your* choice.

Even though it may come to you as an enemy, intent on hurting you, you can convert it into an ally that can help you enormously. Its ability to hurt you will be reduced to almost nothing; instead, it will provide a stronger foundation for your personal and professional growth.

It simply requires that you make a specific choice every time criticism comes your way. As you make that choice, criticism becomes your ally instead of your enemy and you will soon lose all fear of criticism. You will then stop consciously and subconsciously adjusting your words and behaviour to avoid it. You will be free to do whatever it takes to improve any situation or relationship in your life, regardless of the risks.

How does one turn criticism into one's ally? By being like a wise judge and saying to yourself, "I'll take that into consideration." This is a very important line that you should memorise, so say it out loud and clear, right now: "I'll take that into consideration."

The first step, therefore, is not to react, defend, or attack, but to "consider". The next step is the two things you are to "consider"—the source of the criticism and the accuracy of the criticism.

First consider the source. Who said it and why was it said. Is the person qualified to make such a criticism? Does he or she know the background necessary to make a wise and valid criticism? Did that person fully understand what you were doing or saying or the true intentions behind what you said or did before criticising you? Or was s/he simply reacting to what s/he perceived as your intentions? You should also consider if your critic meant exactly what s/he said. For example, if your wife says you are never considerate of her feelings, she does not mean "never". She means in this situation you were not considerate of her feelings in the way she would have liked you to be, and there have been other times when you have not been considerate of her feelings in the way she wanted you to be. If your husband says you always put everyone else's needs above his, he does not really mean "always" and he does not mean everyone. He means you did in this circumstance, and you have at other times in the past.

It is only when you befriend criticism that its harmful effect disappears

For any criticism you receive, considering the source, its qualifications, its intentions and motivations is the first step in turning criticism from an enemy into an ally. For it is only when you befriend criticism that its harmful effect disappears.

The next step in turning criticism into an ally is to consider its accuracy. Criticism is like a bucket full of water. At the very bottom of the water is a little bit of sand and, sometimes, hidden in the sand, are one or more gold nuggets. Whenever someone criticises you, that person is throwing this bucket of water into your face. Now, your natural inclination will always be to do one of these three things—duck and run, throw up your arms and defend, or get angry and attack.

While these are all natural inclinations, they are all wrong reactions. It is only a bucket of water, not a bucket of cement.

No one has ever been critically injured being splashed with a bucket of water. And yet some people react by pulling out a gun and shooting the person criticising them. Yes, the water in the face is cold and uncomfortable for a few moments, but it is still only water. Grab a towel and dry off.

As far as the sand goes, if a little gets in your eyes, it will momentarily distort your vision and cause your eyes to tear. It will cloud your judgement. Clear the sand out of your eyes and take the matter under consideration by looking at the source and accuracy of the criticism. Do not instantly react.

And now comes the good part: As you consider the accuracy of the criticism, you will often find a gold nugget of truth hidden in the sand. When found, that nugget can be turned into value by using the truth to make an improvement in your behaviour, attitude or words—an improvement that will raise your level of achievement and fulfilment and take you to success.

The third and final step in turning criticism into your friend is your response to it.

Thus criticism becomes your best friend or worst enemy depending upon its source, its accuracy and your response to it. The world is full of parrots—people who freely give criticism but are not qualified to do so. Remember also that most people criticise others to avoid looking at their own faults and errors.

But that is not your responsibility or mine. Our responsibility is to take control of how we respond to each and every criticism that comes our way. Let them throw their buckets of water at you. Step back, consider the source and the accuracy, wipe the sand out of your eyes and look for the gold nuggets.

Do this, and criticism will soon become one of your best friends, providing you with added wisdom and faster and more mature personal and professional growth. In the beginning, you will have to work hard not to react and to instead respond correctly. But if you work at it for a few months, then responding correctly to criticism will become a positive habit and ally that will serve you for the rest of your life. Always remember, a successful person is one who turns criticism into something constructive.

Obstacle 4: *Lacking a clear and precise vision*

If you do not have a clear picture of your destination and a precise map to get there, you will not even begin the trip. And any trip you begin will not get you very far.

Imagine for a moment that you live in California. One day the mailman knocks on your door and hands you a certified letter. You open it and you discover that it is a personal letter from Donald Trump. In this letter, he tells you that he wants you and another

> ★ A successful person is one who turns criticism into something constructive ★

person to come to New York and be his guests for one week. He is going to put you up in a beautiful suite in the finest hotel. He will give you $5,000 a day. You will have a limousine at your disposal and you will be dining with your favourite movie star one night, and your favourite recording star the next. The following week, you and your guest will be flown first-class to any destination in Europe, for a ten-day vacation of a lifetime.

As you approach the end of this letter, you are so excited you can hardly see straight. You then come to the last paragraph, which reads as follows: "The only catch is that you must drive from your house to my house, and you must not use any map at any time. Further, you cannot ask anyone for directions. In fact, my friend Vikas Malkani will be at your door presently to escort you on your trip to make sure you are not tempted to use a map or ask directions. Finally, you have one week to reach my house and claim your prize."

You read that paragraph and your response might be, "That's ridiculous! There's no way on earth I could get from here to there and then to his house without a map and without asking for directions. It's totally impossible!"

Well, if this were your reaction, you would be right. If you had all the time in the world, you might make it. But you would waste a lot of time and fuel, and it might take months or years. Then, once you arrive, you would still be looking for the house.

And finding Donald Trump's house without a specific address, map, or asking directions, would take you even longer.

Would you even attempt to start the trip? Of course not. It would be a total waste of time and there would be absolutely no chance of seeing your dream fulfilled.

> ☆ If you do not define your dreams in writing and chart a map to reach them, you will never achieve any of them ☆

Now, suppose the last paragraph of Donald Trump's letter was a little different. It said you cannot use any existing map and you cannot ask for directions along the way, but before you start on the trip, you could make one telephone call to Donald Trump's office in order to get the directions that would tell you every road, highway and turn to take, right from your front door to his.

Now here is the critical question: When the time came to call Donald Trump's office to get his address and those precise directions, would you have a pen and a pad of paper ready to write down every detail? Or, would you simply listen to the directions and trust your memory?

The answer is obvious: Of course you would write them down. Receiving your dream vacation would depend upon it. You would then create your own map from what you wrote down. Once you began your trip you would consult your map and notes along every step of the way to make sure you stayed right on track all the way to your destination.

By simply defining your destination, writing down the address and directions and creating your own simple map, you would arrive at Donald Trump's house in plenty of time to claim your dream vacation.

I share with you this story to illustrate several points that you must understand if you ever want to get yourself off the base station and begin to achieve your most awesome dreams. The first lesson this story gives is how impossible it is to reach a destination, no matter how great the reward, without first getting an address and precisely following a map each step of the way.

The second lesson of the story is this: If you would be willing to take all of these simple steps—defining your destination, writing down the directions, creating a map—just to achieve your dream vacation, how much more should you be willing to do the same thing, to achieve your dreams in the most important areas of your personal and professional life? After all, is it not *your* life? And what you accomplish with it is worth infinitely more than a seventeen-day dream vacation.

If you are like the vast majority of adults who will never take off in the direction of their dreams, chances are you have not defined them in writing. You certainly have not written down the directions or charted a map on how to achieve those dreams of yours.

I can promise you that if you do not define your dreams in writing and chart a map to reach them, you will never achieve any of them.

Writing your dreams down and prioritising them is like creating an address book for your dreams

Your first reaction may be: "It sounds so hard and would take so much time," or you may say to yourself, "I don't even know what my dreams are."

Well, the good news is that once you begin to think about your dreams, you will find that defining them is not only easier than you think, it is a lot of fun.

And it does not take a lot of time. Initially, it may require a few sittings of, say, fifteen to thirty minutes each, but after that, you will only need a few minutes per week.

Charting a Precise Map to Your Dreams

Of the six obstacles that keep you anchored to mediocrity, this one is the easiest to cut. Your cutting tool can be a notebook and pen, a day planner or your computer. The procedure itself is so simple; it may be hard for you to believe that it will actually work. Our goal here is not to begin the trip, but simply to get a specific address for each dream and to define it in writing.

You will then have a map in hand with which to pursue your dream and a very specific, plotted course on which to measure your progress every day, week and month of your journey to that dream.

The first thing you need to do in defining your dreams is to create on a single sheet of paper a simple list of the most significant areas in your life, starting with the most important and working down. For example:

1. My marriage
2. My business and career
3. My children
4. My health
5. My family's health, happiness, security and future
6. My extracurricular activities and passions

After you have created your list, designate a sheet of paper for each item and write that item at the top. On each page (you may need several pages for each category), write as many dreams as you can think of for that particular category. They do not have to be prioritised; just write them down as you think of them, and be as general or as specific as you like. After you have created your dream page in any area, go back and number each of those dreams, according to its priority.

Writing your dreams down and prioritising them is like creating an address book for your dreams. You have defined them and placed them in order of importance. And with these maps in hand, you will be amazed at how quickly you will be able to begin to achieve dreams that you have never dared hope to achieve.

Obstacle 5: *Lacking know-how*

"I don't know how!" "I wouldn't even know where to start." "I could never do that, I don't even have a clue how to do it."

These statements represent an obstacle everyone confronts, namely, a lack of know-how. How many men and women give up on relationships because they simply do not know what to do when it comes to figuring out what their partner needs or wants, or how to take a relationship that is not working and make it work a whole lot better?

When successful people are confronted with a situation that reveals their ignorance, they will tend to hear a call to action and creative thinking

The majority of adults surrender or retreat when confronted with a situation that reveals their lack of know-how. Even though everyone lacks know-how in some area or the other, in reality, this is usually only a perceived obstacle.

When successful people are confronted with a situation that reveals their ignorance, they will tend to hear a call to action and creative thinking. Do you think Thomas Edison had know-how when he began to pursue his dream of creating electric light? He did not. That is why it took over ten thousand attempts before he finally achieved his dream. But he did achieve it in the end.

A lack of know-how is as common to human experience as breathing. And yet, the vast majority of adults view it as Mount Everest in a snowstorm—an impossible obstacle to overcome. Sir Edmund Hillary rightly pointed out: "It is not the mountain we conquer, but ourselves." So do not view your lack of awareness as a major block. Also remember that just because an obstacle is perceived in a certain way, it does not mean that no attempt should be made to conquer it.

Instead of being an insurmountable obstacle, a lack of knowledge in any situation can become a springboard to unimaginable success and achievement. In fact, I usually have far greater success in areas where I have absolutely no knowledge than I ever could in areas where I have a little knowledge. Why? Because when I honestly face a problem where I have no know-how, I immediately look for an expert who has more knowledge in that area than I will ever have.

Each and every one of us has a limited number of strengths, talents and abilities, and yet we have an infinite number of weaknesses and inabilities. Said another way, what we do know and can do is much less than what we do not know and cannot do. If we cannot find a way to convert our weaknesses and inabilities from obstacles into strengths, we will never achieve anything beyond mediocrity. So if you want to graduate from the masses who rarely achieve their dreams, you must first admit that you only have a few strengths, talents and abilities, and a lot of weaknesses and inabilities. That is the first step.

The second step is to identify your strengths, talents and abilities and your weaknesses and inabilities. In addition to using your own mind to identify these, ask for guidance from those who know you the best. They will help you identify areas you would otherwise completely overlook. The way one acts and reacts to situations is often strongly influenced, if not outright dictated, by one's personality type. And each personality type has tremendous strengths and significant weaknesses.

★ Your limited resources never have to be viewed as insurmountable obstacles to your dreams and goals ★

Once you understand your type and its natural inclinations, you can begin to play to your strong points, strengthen your weaknesses, and partner with people whose personality types complement yours. Focus your attention on yourself and begin to honestly see what you are like. Self-analyse, identify and then accept the wonderful ramifications of knowing your strengths and weaknesses. An individual's personality type reveals his or her natural inclinations, strengths and weaknesses. It also determines how he or she will naturally respond in most given situations.

As you focus on your dominant strengths and weaknesses, it is critical that you understand that these traits are natural inclinations. Weaknesses and negative inclinations can be strengthened, balanced, compensated for, or even eliminated, by choosing to do what is right and best in a situation rather than simply letting your personality's natural inclination dictate behaviour. You can choose to cultivate the strengths that bring you the greatest benefit and choose to avoid your natural weaknesses. Once you know that you have a natural bias or tendency to act in a certain way, you can be on the alert and balance your natural tendency by modifying your behaviour.

As is the case with your lack of know-how, your natural inclination will be to view your weaknesses as difficult or even insurmountable obstacles standing between you and your dreams. All you need, in fact, is to change your view of your weaknesses from being insurmountable obstacles to becoming springboards to success and wealth. As you learn to use your weaknesses, inabilities and a lack of know-how as springboards, the fifth obstacle that has kept you anchored will be completely and permanently severed.

Obstacle 6: *Lacking resources*

You cannot launch your ship all by yourself. Failure to recruit the right outside resources always makes setting sail totally impossible. "I would love to do that, but I don't have the money!" "I would love to start my own business, but I'm not a good salesman!" "Where does the day go? There just aren't enough hours in the day!" "I know I need to start exercising, but I just don't have the time!"

These statements reveal a "lack of resources" that these people believe they need to overcome in order to achieve a goal or fulfil a dream. This obstacle is right next to a lack of know-how in its strength and the consequences it produces. Like the lack of know-how, the lack of resources appears to many as insurmountable obstacles. When a lack of resources stands between people and their dreams, their normal response is to turn around and walk away from those dreams. The comment, "I would love to do that, but I don't have the money!" points to the one resource no one ever feels they have enough of—money. No matter how much you have, it is never enough. Money represents a limited resource to all.

We must be the change we wish to see

"I would love to start my own business, but I'm not a good salesman," reveals another limited resource that plagues us all—talent and ability. Bill Gates is obviously talented, and yet a recent article in *Forbes* says that Microsoft would be only a fraction of what it is today if it was not for the talents and abilities of his partners. But when you squander time, you can never get it back, not a single minute. Time is your most valuable commodity. No matter how much money you have, no matter how talented you are, once time has passed, it is gone for good. Even worse, your time in the future is equally limited and becomes more limited and valuable with every passing day. I share this with you because it is my fervent hope that by the time you finish reading this book, you will have a much greater awareness and appreciation of all your limited resources, especially your time. This would guide your behaviour in a way to make the absolute best use of your resources.

Your limited resources never have to be viewed as insurmountable obstacles to your dreams and goals. Instead, like your lack of know-how, they can become an aid to achieving your loftiest dreams. There are five important points that you must always keep in mind:

1. Your three most limited resources are time, talent and money.

2. You can expand your limited resources by seeking outside help. You can expand your time by delegating work and duties; you can expand your talents by recruiting those who have the expertise and experience you lack and you can expand your money by arranging for help from banks, investors, financers, friends, family and so on.

3. If time is an obstacle, write down any of your current activities that could be delegated to someone else so as to free up more of your time.

4. If your lack of talent is an obstacle, write down the kinds of talents you need to find in others.

5. If money is an obstacle, write down the possible sources you might recruit to gain the money necessary to achieve that dream.

To end this chapter let me give you the example of a man of great strength who started with great weaknesses and yet became one of the most significant leaders of the world. Using complete non-violence, he went up against the most powerful military empire of his times and took one of the largest and most populated countries of the world to freedom and independence. The man I talk about is known as Mahatma (Great Soul) Gandhi, the father of India. Short, frail and clad in simple handmade clothes, Mahatma Gandhi brought the mightiest colonial, military empire the world had ever seen to its knees without lifting a finger in anger or violence.

His life was full of trials and tribulations, but his destination was very clear and he had charted his map to the final end. He stuck to it with passionate persistence and persevered till he had achieved his goals, and given millions of people their freedom from oppression.

Here are some secrets from his remarkable journey to success; a journey that serves as an example worth emulating for people from all areas of life.

Leadership Lessons from Gandhi's Life

A careful study of the life of the non-violent and frail Gandhi reveals very focussed and powerful leadership qualities. Here are ten that I have identified for the benefit of all achievers:

1. Gandhi had charisma: He was different from others and believed in himself strongly.

2. Gandhi had a compelling vision: He set a clear target for himself. He was also self-motivated.

3. Gandhi was simple and direct: He was easy to understand and follow.

4. Gandhi had a willingness to make and follow hard choices: He took decisions, made choices and demonstrated a whatever-it-takes attitude.

5. Gandhi had a mission: He set a goal that motivated others, gave them freedom and power.

6. Gandhi set a clear strategy: To reach the goal he planned a clear strategy and communicated it to others.

7. Gandhi was persistent: Once his mind was set, he stuck to his target with crab-like persistence, changing only if a better way showed itself.

8. Gandhi understood people's minds and hearts: He cared for those around him and understood how they felt and what they thought. He respected them.

9. Gandhi capitalised on opportunity: He was quick to spot opportunity and to seize it to his advantage.

10. Gandhi was patient: He was willing to wait for the reward of his efforts. He knew that the strong man is a patient man indeed.

As is evident, Mahatma Gandhi was no ordinary man. His life was a success because he rose above mediocrity and left many valuable lessons for us. Here was a man who changed the very course of history because he had the innate strength to face all obstacles.

Gandhi's life was a success because he chose to give meaning to it. He led the way; he defined the path. He was quick to reject mediocrity in all aspects of life. His thoughts were lofty; his vision even more. As he himself put it, "We must be the change we wish to see."

Success Secret 5

Choose excellence!

Millionaires reject mediocrity

|Chapter Six|

Dare to be Different

Wherever you see a successful business, someone once made a courageous decision.

Peter Drucker

Fear is a state of mind. Courage is a state of mind, too. You have a choice between these two.

Having a courageous state of mind enables you to be a leader. When you are brave, you are likely to give the world something to react to, instead of just reacting to what the world dumps in your lap. You are more naturally oriented towards doing what is right, in the right way, for the right reasons. A courageous state of mind turns failures into building blocks for growth; it prompts active participation. It makes you different and it makes you special.

It is one thing to have courage in the face of uncontrollable situations that fill you with fear; it is another to seek opportunities that have the potential for generating fear.

Having a success mindset requires a willingness to be bold, to dare to depart from standard operational procedures and to have the courage to stand forth. Similarly, your head might be filled with dreams but without the courage to take action, these dreams will never really be actualised.

> Fear is a state of mind. Courage is a state of mind, too

It is paradoxical that in school we are taught to follow the rules. We are categorically told to get in line, be quiet, and memorise the right answers. In the corporate world, however, we are rewarded for making a difference, thinking for ourselves and challenging protocol. Here, differentiation is rewarded, not similarity! We are encouraged to think out of the box; we are told, again and again, that the successful men and women are those who know how to differentiate. They are unique because they dare to be different. They also will not make excuses or blame others when things go wrong.

When life presents a challenge, most of us tend to look for rocks to hide under, when we could be using the challenges to learn, grow and get stronger. Instead of taking action, we make excuses. Excuses are simply your reason not to make things happen; they are apologies for not having courage. In other words, excuses are ways of making ourselves feel better about being faint of heart; they are what we use to justify our lack of action. Most of the time, excuses have little basis in reality. They are little more than fear enhancers. Recognise them for what they are and you will take a big step towards breaking free.

Let's consider how babies learn to walk. They hold on to something that looks sturdy, pull themselves up, maybe take a step and then fall. They repeat the process again and again. They soon figure out something about balance and something else about moving their feet in sequence until, finally, everything comes together and they embark on legs suddenly capable of carrying them to a variety of new challenges. Before you know it they are running.

There is a lesson here for us. Like children learning how to walk, a successful person is one who stumbles, maybe even falls, but gets up and gets going. The successful know that without action, nothing is achieved. Too often, the problem is that, while our legs are willing, our minds and hearts are not. Instead of moving forward and risking failure, we cosy up with our apologies. Over time, we condition ourselves to play it safe. We swallow impulses and resist the spirit of adventure, discovery and curiosity that came naturally to us as children. We play it safe because we are afraid to tread into the unknown. Thus we never achieve more than what we have been accustomed to.

One reason so many of us avoid taking action is that we are unwilling to experience even the slightest bit of pain or discomfort. So we decide that the best way is the safe way. And we think the safe way is to do nothing. But we are fooling ourselves—because not taking action is still taking an action. The successful know that playing it safe is risky. If you have a desire for recognition and fame, for reaching a level of excellence, for earning enormous material rewards or even simply for being the very best at something, the answers to these questions will show you the way forward. Remember the age-old adage—well begun is half done. Begin with the right perspective and your journey is already smoother than the rest.

A courageous state of mind turns failures into building blocks for growth

To find the purpose of your life, which is the beginning of the road to achievement, ask yourself these four questions:

1. *What do I love to do?*

Here you have to ask yourself: What work fills me with joy? What chosen field of action can I throw my heart and soul into? You need to discover your deepest driving desire. Considering that work consumes a large portion of our time every day, it is imperative that we enjoy the work we do. You can never be excellent at something you do not enjoy doing. Successful men and women develop a passion for their work, their endeavour.

2. *What would I do for free?*

Ask yourself: What would I be willing to do for free even if initially I was unable to charge for it?

For successful men and women, their work is their play. If you do what you love, your work is your play, and then you never have to work a single day in your life. It is imperative that you enjoy the work you do if you want to become excellent at it. Without joy, your heart will never be in it. Do the work for the sake of the work, and then find a way to charge for it.

3. *What am I better than others at?*

Ask yourself: What is the area or the field where I have an unfair advantage over others? Where do my special abilities and talents pull me? What am I naturally good at? What do I do that is better than others? Find this area and then improve yourself even more in it. This is your natural strength; build on it. It will take you to your treasure.

4. *How do others see my talents and gifts?*

Before starting to work in an effortless, exuberant state, we must first know ourselves to be able to consciously choose the correct vocation. Check your attitudes and feelings about your work with those whom you respect. Sometimes, others can see from a distance what you cannot see up close. Study and consider an outside view on your talents, vocation and job before you decide to take the plunge. Once you've begun, don't give up till you reach where you want to be.

Before you lies a world of infinite ideas and opportunities—avenues that will satisfy your appetite for success and happiness. But during the course of your life, you must ask yourself and answer the four questions of greatness; the answers are the keys to superior achievement. Finding these answers calls for no special effort. These four questions make no unreasonable demands upon your time or ability. But make no mistake: If you are to experience all that life holds, you must decide now upon your purpose. Remember, your life's purpose will not be revealed through any one of these answers alone, but your answers are keys to unlocking the secret of your true purpose.

★ Once you've begun, don't give up till you reach where you want to be ★

These questions represent the final door through which all must pass to attain greatness. Each answer will provide a key that will unlock this door. These keys will be in your hands when you have prepared yourself to accept them. From this moment on, and for what remains of your life, make a commitment to answer these questions and uncover your life's purpose. In the process, you will find out what makes you different. And it is this difference, the qualities that make you unique, that will help you succeed in your chosen path. They will not only define your vision, they will underline your reason for being. Without vision, your actions have no direction. Remember, you have but one life to live.

Success Secret 6

Differentiate yourself!

Millionaires take action on their uniqueness

| Chapter Seven |

Follow Your Heart

I realise that I don't have limits. Limits are always influences that come from outside, from people who don't believe in themselves and their abilities. I firmly believe in myself. I know that I can do whatever I want and that I'll always reach my goals.

Madonna

Changing the world, even your small corner of it, is hard work. You have to be motivated to make a difference. And you need courage—more courage, maybe, than you think you have.

We all run into fearful situations that provoke instant reactions. When a fire breaks out, when you get a call from the police notifying you of an automobile accident, when you get any kind of bad news, you have an instinctive response. You do not have time to think rationally. You cannot break your fear apart and tackle it one piece at a time. Your response in times of trial flows from your values. Your reactions are based on your belief of what separates right from wrong.

Remember, one of the richest sources of courage is the fundamental belief in the rightness of your cause. And this belief often stems from the fact that you are listening to your inner voice, that you are following your heart and its dictates.

Values provide a framework for living. They make it possible to weigh options and make decisions you will not regret. When you make choices that are aligned with your values, you build your character and sense of self-worth. When you compromise your values, you are living a lie.

★ One of the richest sources of courage is the fundamental belief in the rightness of your cause ★

The stronger your values are, the more stable and secure you will be. That is, you are the sum of your personality, your upbringing, everything that has ever happened to you and the ways in which you have reacted. Sometimes, when we align ourselves with a collection of people, our individual values become blurred. At its worst, we get swept up in what historians and newscasters call mob mentality. The mere act of being a part of it can wear away your identity because the natural tendency is to blend in, to run with the pack.

Again, you are always only yourself. You are not defined by your associates or where you work. Never forget this. It is because of what you have or have not done that you are who you are and where you are.

Four Steps to Attain Great Victory in Life

Greatness, it seems, harbours heroes—resilient and resourceful. One of the first lessons of life is to learn how to wrestle victory from defeat, to transform shattered dreams into plans of action. When faced with humiliation and disaster, it takes mental toughness and stamina to sit by and watch your hopes fall from grace. It takes everything you can muster to search through the wreckage and ruins for the elements of future conquests. Yet this measures the difference between those who succeed and those who fail. You cannot measure an individual by his or her failures, but rather by what he or she makes of them.

Many people seem to think that ambition is a quality born within; that it is not susceptible to improvement; that it is something thrust upon us that will guide itself. In reality it is a passion that responds to cultivation. Society watches a child's first failure with deep interest. It is the index of his or her life, the measure of the child's capacity; the mere fact of his or her failure does not generate much concern, but how s/he digests defeat is carefully watched. We are all, in a sense, under observation. There are many out there who would be quite delighted if you were to fail. Do not let this deter you.

Just carry on your journey with the goal well defined. The road ahead is always clear; all you have to do is to follow your heart. It will provide you the signposts and lead you to triumph.

Here are the four steps by which you can secure your greatest victory in life. Each step will work, regardless of your level of education or self-esteem. As these steps become the cultivated habits of your daily life, they will enable you to face every challenge with a deeper sense of purpose in yourself and also in your abilities.

Step 1: *Decide what limitations you will accept*

There are two common errors that can devastate your ability to succeed. First, it is a mistake to assume that all limits are self-imposed; second, it is equally foolish and self-defeating to knuckle under self-imposed limits.

Surviving the odds involves choosing which limitations you will accept and which you will resist. People who drive themselves against their natural limitations tend to become frustrated and embittered. Constant failure beats them down and they lose all semblance of confidence and determination.

Your first step to attaining your greatest victory is to determine what limits are truly limits versus those that are self-imposed.

> ★ It is because of what you have or have not done that you are who you are and where you are ★

Are you absolutely tired of allowing circumstances to define your life? Are you tired of having people tell you what you can or cannot do, or what you should or must do? Perhaps you were brought up in an environment that taught you limitations that accentuated the negative—particularly your mistakes and shortcomings. Yet I know that within you something has told you that you can make it, that you can survive and succeed in spite of the difficulties. Surroundings that others deem unfavourable cannot prevent the unfolding of your powers. You can have anything you want if you develop a consciousness to obtain it. The successful know that success is created inside them far before it shows up externally in their lives.

God grant me the serenity to accept the things I cannot change;
The courage to change the things I can change;
And the wisdom to know the difference.

This old prayer from Saint Francis of Assisi has helped more people sort out where they should place the thrust of their efforts and concerns than any of us can imagine.

Step 2: *Give attention to your greatest strengths*

All achievers have learned the secret of concentrated energy. They are in touch with their inner resources and have discovered what they can do best—what they believe in is worth giving their best to accomplish. It is this belief that helps their self-confidence to grow and their inborn abilities to rise.

The sports world stands in agreement that the one quality that made heavyweight boxing champion Muhammad Ali nearly unbeatable was that he always made his opponent fight his fight. Ali would "float like a butterfly and sting like a bee".

Beneath the poetry and self-adoration lay a great fighter who knew what he could do best and stuck to it. No wonder he made far more powerful fighters believe he was 'The Greatest'.

Take the second step to overcoming the odds: Make the world fight your fight. Focus attention on your greatest strengths.

Focus attention on your greatest strengths

Step 3: *Adopt a positive mental attitude and seek out positive people*

There are two types of people throughout the world—the positive and the negative. Whether you are an optimist or a pessimist, the future lies in your hands, and yours alone. If you want to be joyful, enthusiastic and excited about life, you can be, regardless of your circumstances. The first rule of developing a positive mental attitude is: Act positively, and you will become positive.

You cannot think your way into acting positively, but you can act your way into thinking positive. Welcome every morning with a smile. Be a self-starter. Allow your first hour to set the tone of success and positive action that is certain to resonate through the entire day. Practise ridding your mind of all negative, self-defeating thoughts; discipline your mind to work for you.

The second part of this rule suggests that you must seek out and associate with other positive individuals. Be very careful when choosing the kind of people with whom you associate because, whether you realise it or not, they strongly influence your life. People who believe that things cannot be done will set out to prove themselves right. But men and women who know things can be done go out and make them happen.

As you begin to spend time with like-minded people—positive, upbeat men and women—they will reinforce your attitudes about life. Greet everyone you meet with love and laughter; be gentle, kind and courteous towards friend and foe. People who respect themselves and their abilities help nurture your capabilities and your self-esteem.

If misery loves company, do not be a part of it.

Whatever you attain in life will be based upon your faith; your belief in yourself. Be willing to take risks. You cannot discover new oceans unless you have the courage to lose sight of the shore. Do not be afraid to dream big dreams. Take advantage of what this universe and your country have to offer. Get a dream, and then lock on to it with intensified focus. Seek knowledge. Seek experience. You may not have all the answers, but someone does. Find these people and make their strengths yours by partnering with them.

You must develop an attitude that lifts your sights from the ordinary to the extraordinary. You must develop an attitude that gives you hope, that inspires you to attempt the impossible, that challenges you to grow. And, most important of all, you must learn to put your heart and your soul into what you do. There is an oft-quoted adage: "Throw your heart over the fence and the rest of you will follow!" Make a choice to live from your heart and ask your mind to chart the path to your dreams.

A winning and positive attitude is the world's most desperate need at this point in time. There are no hopeless situations, only people who think hopelessly. The only way you can lose in life is if you defeat yourself mentally. Your own self-doubts or the opinions of others can stifle your abilities and any possibility of achievement. Self-confidence is often little more than a feeling deep down in the pit of your stomach that you can do something that reason says is impossible. But, as you respond positively to that feeling, it grows and grows until it reaches full bloom in concrete action.

You are unique, one of a kind, and you must bring out your uniqueness and shine it for the whole world to see

Step 4: *Commit to reaching your full potential*

If you are to reach your full potential, you must cultivate the creative urges within you and respond to the sensitivity that cries out for expression. The greatest enemy of your creative powers is your complacency—being satisfied with less than what you are capable of doing. You must find positive ways to express your individuality. You are unique, one of a kind, and you must bring out your uniqueness and shine it for the whole world to see. In other words, people who accept themselves are not preoccupied with what others think about them. They are willing to express those traits and inner feelings that give them their uniqueness, without an undue regard for what anyone else thinks.

People with strong positive self-images are satisfied to be themselves, regardless of what others think, say, or do.

The human mind, coupled with an indomitable spirit and a physical body, is capable of creating in a way that is unknown anywhere in the universe. Even when the physical body is limited in certain key areas, the human mind and spirit can break free to carve out success in the most amazing ways.

But before you reach that level of being, you must face one of life's most difficult questions: Who is holding you back?

The only true answer to this question is: None but you yourself!

Seven Success Skills from Jesus

One of the great leaders of our world has to be Jesus Christ. Today, over two thousand years after his death, his teachings are continuing to transform people all over the planet as are those of the many other spiritual masters of our world.

Jesus led a team of twelve to reach out and influence the whole world. He was highly motivated himself and carried a self-belief so strong that it stood firm even in physical torture and immense pain. He used tried and tested management and leadership principles to motivate his team to reach their chosen goals with focus and persistence. In the face of tremendous opposition, he persevered and continued to perform his actions passionately till he reached his goals.

You need only to look at a world-transforming personality such as Jesus to see the beliefs and awareness necessary for manifesting both inner and outer success. As you follow his life, right from his childhood years onwards, you will realise that:

★ There are no hopeless situations, only people who think hopelessly ★

1. Jesus respected the law of sowing and reaping. He knew that everything begins with a seed to sow; that the seed you sow can create the future God has promised you. The seeds you sow today determine the manifestation of your future.

2. Jesus had a passionate commitment to his cause. He clearly expressed his vision with total self-belief. He always believed he had his father (God) with him. He continued to believe and follow his vision even when others didn't.

3. Jesus took decisive action. He was always working to create new ways of thinking; he was always thinking of new ways to share his vision and dreams with his team and those around him. He was a man not only of words, but also of constant action.

4. Jesus believed in discipline. He knew that true leadership requires restraint and his life was an example of this

quality. He first disciplined himself and then expected others to follow.

5. Jesus saw things differently. His beliefs and ideas were not always in agreement with the society around him. He saw the whole picture, the long view. He was bold. He was willing to go where he had never been before. He saw things that could be, and should be, and worked to make them a reality.

6. Jesus worked through his fears. He knew that everyone feels fearful about something. And that the best way to conquer fear was to constantly move forward.

   In addition, he accepted fear as an ever-present fact of life but refused to be halted by it. He simply refused to be discouraged when others misjudged his motives. He knew that success is on the other side of scorn and false accusations.

7. Jesus believed in the power of prayer. He prayed often, and in gratitude. He connected back constantly with his higher source. He asked for guidance and help openly. He kept in regular touch with his boss, his Creator. He had internal anchors that he sought his strength and determination from. He was centred within himself and guarded his valuable energy, his inner core. Jesus lived in an attitude of gratitude.

And yes, underscoring these seven skills was the fact that Jesus always followed his heart. It was the voice within, that direct connection with his soul, which led him to go beyond limits. Jesus had all the traits of a successful individual because he lived the way he chose. He listened to the call of his heart.

The seeds you sow today determine the manifestation of your future

That is the way successful people have to live. They have to follow the voice that emanates from the inner recesses of their hearts—a voice that tells them what is the right thing to do, despite many temptations and other odds and obstacles along the way.

So get going—it's an exciting arena out there and you can easily win.

Success Secret 7

Listen to your inner voice!

Millionaires constantly expand their limits

| Chapter Eight |

Never Give Up

We gain strength, and courage, and confidence by each experience in which we really stop and look fear in the face...we must do that which we think we cannot.

Eleanor Roosevelt

I define dedication as action that does not give up but rather improves with every attempt. As you begin to walk the path to your dreams and take constantly improved action, you will be faced with many obstacles and hindrances. Obstacles will present themselves to challenge you and your determination. Without dedication within you, you will be tempted to cut and run at the first sight or taste of trouble. Dedication is what keeps you going even when you feel like giving up. It is a secret of those who are successful and reach their dreams.

Without dedication, no worthwhile goal is ever achieved.

Thus it is necessary that you dedicate yourself to your cause. Once you have dedicated yourself to your chosen goal and you have done everything else that you could think of, all you can now do is to let luck take its course.

And the only way luck can be of any help at all to you is if you are in the arena, taking chances. If you are sitting on the sidelines watching, luck does not matter.

Good luck comes to those who are dedicated to their mission. Successful people know luck does not just happen; it is an ancillary benefit of being actively dedicated to a mission. For instance, you will not get lucky and find the job of your dreams if you spend all your time on the couch watching television. On the other hand, there is no certainty of you getting lucky and finding a job even if every day for three months you mail half-a-dozen résumés, knock on doors and network with people who work in the area of your interest.

★ Without dedication, no worthwhile goal is ever achieved ★

So understand this: The amount of good luck you have coming to you is in direct proportion to the number of chances you take. You have to keep at it, walking the extra mile—taking risks and going where others actually fear to tread. There is an element of pure random chance in every situation. Preparation, dedication, faith and commitment can reduce the percentage of your fate that is determined by pure chance, but they cannot eliminate it totally. Similarly, you cannot plan for luck, it usually comes as a bolt out of the blue. But you can be ready for it. You also have to let it happen. To do that, you have to believe.

It helps to have a childlike faith in your mission. Imagine how you would act if you knew it was impossible for you to fail.

It is not hard to dedicate yourself when you have taken up a challenge and you have notched up an unbroken string of successes. You are finding plenty of positive reinforcement—naturally, you will have the energy to persevere. When you are thinking positively, the world crackles with possibilities and seems to support everything you do. Probably the best part about thinking positively is that it kindles courage.

Positive thinking cannot help but put you in a courage mode almost without you having to think about it.

That is because when you think positively, you believe in yourself. And you are a whole lot more likely to risk failure in order to achieve. When you believe that it will work out, you have the courage to dedicate yourself despite a run of bad luck. This is the essence of courage.

So bad luck (or unwanted results) is not necessarily a bad thing. Bad luck can be a stepping stone to good luck. Besides, the more bad luck you have, the greater are the odds of receiving good luck. It can help to build your courage because every time you pick yourself up, dust yourself off and try again, your resistance to fear increases and on your next attempt, you will be stronger, more focussed and more experienced—all qualities that allow you to score a direct hit on your target.

You can expect the worst; in which case, you will never be disappointed. Or you can hope for the best.

When you dwell on the negative, you experience failure, pain and defeat in your mind, over and over again. We make our own realities and then wonder how they came to be.

★ The amount of good luck you have coming to you is in direct proportion to the number of chances you take ★

This is true because of a very simple and ancient spiritual law: As you think, so you become. In other words: Whatever you focus on, grows.

However, by this very law, when you dwell on the positive, you experience the feeling of failure only once, and then, only if it actually occurs. Instead you give your energy and attention to the positive outcome that you want. You give your life force to the dream that you want to make a reality. If you believe in yourself, good things have a way of happening.

Let me reiterate: Focus, focus, focus, and then focus some more.

When you look a fear square in the eye, far more often than not, it will back away. And once you have got a fear backing away, you are on the way to declaring victory. But you have to screw up a whole lot of concentration to look a strong and overpowering fear straight in the eye in the first place. You have to focus, focus and focus some more, until your glare burns with the intensity of a laser beam.

One effective method for honing, buffing and otherwise enhancing your power of concentration is through healthy competition. The thing about healthy competition as opposed to regular depleting competition is that it can turn fear into fuel. Healthy competition is when you are centred within yourself but still choose to challenge yourself against another or a set standard, simply as a game or a play.

The mere act of racing against time and around obstacles causes some sort of mental gland to kick in that zaps you with energy, which in turn adds to your courage quotient. Of course, the distinction between fear and exhilaration can be a fine line. If you can channel your fear with a sense of adventure or healthy competition, it quickly becomes exciting.

The point of using competition is to distract yourself from negative thoughts and focus on the task at hand. This works largely because competition counters that part of human nature that insists on dwelling much more than is required on a task or a fear. Competition limits choice. Competition puts you in a mindset that says, "I have to."

Given too many choices, we tend to become confused. A sense of security makes us complacent; instead of taking charge of the matter at hand, we begin to relax and feel that all will be well without our accepting responsibility. Instead of instinctively responding to challenges, we sift our experience through such filters as "Is it professional?" or "What will the neighbours think?" or "Someone like me has no business trying something like that."

If you believe in yourself, good things have a way of happening

Whether you perceive a risk as an opportunity or a reason to curl up into a ball of hopeless paralysis depends largely on your state of mind. If you want to fire up your courage, use the fear of defeat to push yourself to try harder. Turn your task into a challenge, a game, a contest, a race. Keep your eye on the goal and push yourself to reach it.

Never forget that nothing you ever want to achieve can be accomplished without action.

It has long been known that your knowledge is only as deep as your action is. This is true for your dreams as well. Our dreams are of no meaning or consequence if we are unwilling to take action and follow through on them.

This power of action to create the reality of our life has been referred to as the law of karma (action) since time immemorial. Let me explain it for you in simple steps. It is imperative that you understand how this law works for you to become successful in your desires and dreams.

Let us just backtrack here and identify the two greatest motivating factors in anyone's life—the desire for gain and the fear of loss. These two factors are the engines that power your actions. The desire for gain, which includes any kind of gain (love, security, acceptance, success, material goods and wealth, physical appearance, health, spirituality, intimacy with God or a person and so on) and the fear of loss, which includes any kind of loss (love, person, security, acceptance, success, material goods and wealth, physical appearance, health, spirituality and intimacy with God or another person) are the two greatest internal motivating factors in anyone's life. So, if we are to gain the motivation to act, we must always appeal to either our or another person's desire for gain or the inherent fear of loss.

Every person has a different set of values and priorities. In business, people desire gain in their careers, as well as with their customers and projects and so on. They, of course, also fear losing their careers and customers. A person who values time with the family above all things may have very few fears or desires in the area of material wealth. Appealing to the areas of greatest individual concern will increase the persuasiveness of your appeal.

The Secret of Success

Success, both inner and outer, is dependent on certain laws, primary among them is the law based on action or karma. This law states: "As you sow, so shall you reap!" If you study the depths of this law carefully, you come to certain realisations, all very important to the understanding and pursuit of success.

To create success in your life, you must accept that:

> Our dreams are of no meaning or consequence if we are unwilling to take action and follow through on them

1. You have to sow if you want to reap.

2. You will reap only if, and after, you sow.

3. There is a certain gestation period between the time you sow and when you reap.

4. You will reap only that what you sow.

5. Therefore, sow the good seeds, the ones of your choice.

6. Keep tending to and reinforcing the seeds after you sow them.

7. Believe in yourself, but also trust the higher power to support you in your endeavours.

Success Secret 8

Act as if it was impossible to fail!

Millionaires don't let failure become their reality

| Chapter Nine |

Be Persistent, Not Stupid

Success is how high you bounce when you've hit bottom.

General George S. Patton Jr.

Many are confused as to what persistence really is. I am often asked in my seminars, "Does persistence mean you keep doing the same thing till you succeed?"

To this my reply is straightforward: "True persistence is hitting the brick wall, getting up, dusting yourself off, and realising that you are not going to get through it; so you have to figure out a way to get over it, under it, around it, or to blow it up. It is not hitting a brick wall, getting up off the ground, dusting yourself off, and then hitting it again and again and again. That is not persistence, it is stupidity!"

Persistence involves constantly improving your action and making it more and more effective. Making it more effective involves achieving greater results with lesser effort. Thus persistence is a process that involves constant improvement and smarter action that relentlessly continues till, finally, the goal is achieved.

Here are some steps to help you build this most valuable of all strengths as an ingrained pattern of habit in your life.

Persistence involves constantly improving your action and making it more and more effective

Step 1: *Gain a vision*

Persistence begins with a vision. The incredible wisdom of Solomon attested to this when he wrote: "Without a vision the people perish." Solomon was not speaking of physical death but rather the death of the soul. Without vision, people lose their joy and passion for life and slip into the quagmire of mediocrity, simply existing or just getting by, rather than truly living.

Before 1849, there were many pioneers in the USA who decided to "go West" to seek out a better life for themselves and their families, but very few made it all the way to California. Their somewhat general dream did not provide enough fuel to persist in such a long and difficult journey. Then, in 1849, gold was discovered, and all of a sudden thousands of families not only started out for California, they persisted through all kinds of terrible conditions, trials and tribulations until they finally reached the gold fields.

You see, unlike the earlier settlers, they were not simply "going West" to fulfil a general dream of a better life. Rather, they had a very specific vision that fuelled their persistence. They were going to search for gold, find it and become rich—or they were going to get rich by supplying goods and services to all the other people who were going for the gold. They had very specific dreams, and they converted those dreams into goals, and then converted their goals into steps, and the steps into tasks. Their passion thus ignited and continually fuelled their persistence. They had all the persistence they needed to overcome mountains and deserts, outlaws and Indians, disease and pestilence.

So the first step to acquiring or developing persistence is gaining a clear vision of a dream.

Step 2: *Dream big and expand your vision*

The next step follows Thomas Edison's example: "Shoot for the moon. Dream big!" This means looking at all the greatest potential benefits and possible ramifications of your dream. For example, if your dream is to have a marriage where all your deepest emotional needs are met and where you are able to meet the deepest needs of your spouse, list the potential ramifications of achieving that dream. In addition to the greater level of joy and fulfilment that you will experience, your children will also gain greater security and fulfilment. They will gain a clear picture of what a marriage should be, seeing how a husband and wife can truly meet each other's deepest needs and desires. You visualise how that will help them to work towards their own fulfilling marriages and, in turn, be a tremendous blessing to their children. You see generations of strong families resulting from the achievement of your dream. You think of the tremendous contribution you and your children will be able to make to others who want the same kind of fulfilling relationships you have. And this relationship could well go ahead and define all your relationships, including those at the workplace. To be successful, you need to work on getting along with others who are often there to help you make your vision into a reality.

Persistence begins with a vision

As you begin to see all the potential benefits of your dream, your broad vision will give you the persistence you need to wade through the hardships and overcome the obstacles that stand between you and your manifested dream.

Step 3: *Spread your vision*

As soon as Edison gained and made a written record of a vision for an invention, with its entire ramifications, he communicated that vision to his staff and workers. He did everything he could to make sure they caught the entire vision. They then became a team of people unified and motivated by the same vision.

When Edison became discouraged and his persistence began to burn out, he wanted to abandon his dream for a new invention. However, one or more of his associates were still charged up with persistence, and their persistence carried him through, until his persistence was reignited.

Solomon echoed this in the fourth chapter of Ecclesiastes. He wrote: "Two are better than one; because they have a good reward for their labour. For if they fall, the one will lift up his fellow: but woe to him that is alone when he falleth; for he hath not another to help him up."

Step 4: *Expect criticism*

No one enjoys criticism or failure, and yet, for those who succeed, they are as much a part of life as eating and drinking. If you really want to develop persistence, you must first begin to expect criticisms and unforeseen results, and be prepared to deal with them in the proper way.

Let us look at how you handle your disappointments. Whether it is at home or on the job, when things do not go the way you want them to, or when you make a mistake or fall flat on your face, what do you do? Check the appropriate responses to the following question:

How do you react when you don't get what you want?

1. Do you become defensive/angry/discouraged/depressed?

2. Do you pout/withdraw/deny/make excuses/rationalise/attack/blame others/blame circumstances?

3. Do you accept responsibility for the incident/analyse, discover and learn from it/seek insights from others/become determined and diligent to try again and not make the same mistake that caused the incident?

Although the reactions in the first question are all fairly routine, it is important to once again realise that you can choose to respond instead of following your inclination and react the wrong way. After you strike out once, you may want to give up rather than face the possibility of striking out again. In a sense, this is returning to the safety of mediocrity.

> If you expect the unexpected to happen, instead of being surprised, you will be prepared

Instead, if you really want to achieve your dreams, after the initial pain of the disappointment subsides, you must analyse why it happened. If you cannot figure it out, you must seek the advice and insights of others.

How you handle other people's problems as well as their disappointments is also critical to achieving your dreams, because your most powerful asset is your ability to effectively partner. If you consistently mishandle the problems of others who are on your team, your partnering ability will lose its power and not bring the desired results. Remember that there will be times when their persistence will keep you going even when yours is non-existent. If you fail to correctly respond to their difficult times, you will deflate their sense of motivation and, consequently, it will not be available to help fuel yours when you need it most. Look at the questions that follow and see if you can recognise how you handle other people's failures.

1. Do you become critical/angry?

2. Do you lecture/advise/criticise/discipline/correct/withdraw/attack?

3. Do you allow recovery time/listen/comfort/encourage/show patience/offer help and partnership?

Here again, the natural inclination will be to react with the attitudes and actions described in question one. However, once again you can choose to respond with the attitudes and activities described in question three. When you do, you will strengthen the person, his or her persistence and loyalty and commitment to you. You will help alleviate all fears of trying again. And, ultimately, you will see him or her begin to succeed in their chosen path. Remember, nobody likes a lecture after a failure or disappointment. They are already hurting and have probably begun to analyse the 'whys' and 'why nots' before you ever get to them. What they need is an ear and a lot of encouragement from you. If you choose to respond to them correctly, you will both be the beneficiaries of your actions.

Step 5: *Expect obstacles and respond creatively*

If you expect the unexpected to happen, instead of being surprised, you will be prepared. For a moment, let us go back to the working definition of persistence I gave you earlier. True persistence is hitting the brick wall, getting up, dusting yourself off, and realising that you are not going to get through it; so you have to figure out a way to get over it, under it, around it, or to blow it up.

The higher the wall, the greater the inclination to walk away from it. But the higher it is, the more creative you have to be in devising an alternative. If you are unable to devise a creative option that works, you need to seek out partners or advisers who can come up with one that does work.

One of the greatest enemies of persistence is impatience

Step 6: *Plan a marathon, not a sprint*

One of the greatest enemies of persistence is impatience, the desire to chase your dreams at a sprinter's pace. Unfortunately, worthwhile dreams are never only a hundred yards away; instead, they are usually miles away. Most people gain a vision or a dream and then run as fast and as hard as they can to catch it. The only problem is they tire out shortly after they begin.

Think back to the last time you saw a hundred-metre sprint. Whether it was the Olympics or your child's track meet, how did the runners look and act after they crossed the winning post? I am sure they all gasped for air, some of them leaned on their knees, others sat or lay down and some just walked around, head down and panting. No matter what shape they were in, they were all out of breath and temporarily exhausted.

Can you imagine what would happen if the moment they crossed the winning post the official told them, "The race isn't over, there are 105 laps around the track to go." Chances are not one of them would start running. And if they did, they would certainly not run very fast. That is because the only thing a marathon and a hundred-metre dash have in common is that they are both races and the participants are running. However, they require completely different training methods and strategies as well as different running styles.

Edison and his staff worked for nearly three years on his electric light project. They worked long days, often sixteen to twenty hours. They solved problems inventors had been struggling with for over fifty years. This was possible because Edison, the master of persistence, knew that gradual steady progress would not only get the job done, but get it done in record time. My favourite example of a man who mastered persistence, and went through life like a marathon, is a man whose résumé says it all.

1. At twenty-one, he saw his first business fail.
2. At twenty-three, he ran for a political office and lost.
3. At twenty-four, he saw his second business fail.
4. At twenty-seven, he had a nervous breakdown.
5. At twenty-nine, he ran for Congress and lost.
6. At thirty-one, he ran for Congress again, and lost again.
7. At thirty-seven, he ran for Congress and won. (At last!)
8. At forty-nine, he ran for the Senate and lost.

Looking at this man's résumé, would you not think he should just give up his dream of a high political office? And yet he did not tire, burn out or give up. His résumé not only shows persistence, it reveals a great deal of patience. In the end, it paid off—for he was none other than Abraham Lincoln who at the age of fifty-one became the sixteenth president of the USA, the one who would have to overcome the greatest obstacles ever faced by an American president—the splitting of the nation.

★ Pursue your dreams like you were running a marathon, no matter how much you are tempted to sprint ★

Pursue your dreams like you were running a marathon, no matter how much you are tempted to sprint! Do not try to complete too many tasks in a day or take too many steps in a week. Take your time to correctly complete each task and step. And complete them at a pace that does not risk an early burnout. Then be patient and see the results pour in.

Success Secret 9

Failures are only lessons in the school of success!

Millionaires persist till they succeed

9 Essential Secrets of Self-Made Millionaires

Success Secret 1

Take responsibility!
Millionaires know and accept their ability to create their life and their reality

Success Secret 2

Believe in yourself!
Millionaires believe that they are special, and have something to contribute

Success Secret 3

Learn constantly!
Millionaires remain lifelong students and learn from their role models

Success Secret 4

Challenge fear!
Millionaires train themselves to be comfortable with risk

Success Secret 5

Choose excellence!

Millionaires reject mediocrity

Success Secret 6

Differentiate yourself!

Millionaires take action on their uniqueness

Success Secret 7

Listen to your inner voice!

Millionaires constantly expand their limits

Success Secret 8

Act as if it was impossible to fail!

Millionaires don't let failure become their reality

Success Secret 9

Failures are only lessons in the school of success!

Millionaires persist till they succeed

About the Author

Born and brought up in a business family in India, Vikas Malkani was the head of a large business enterprise when Awakening struck him at the age of 29. He has been called many things over the years: Spiritual Guru, Zen Master, Motivator, Mystic, Rich Monk, TV celebrity, Soul Coach and Reiki Master, to name a few. Other than that he is the founder of SoulCentre and a best-selling author.

Today, Vikas is considered one of the world's leading contemporary spiritual teachers. He teaches people to be successful in all aspects of life: the physical, emotional, mental and spiritual. His forte is to make the ancient wisdom of the spiritual masters simple to understand and easy to apply to create a life of health, harmony and abundance on all levels.

Vikas is a disciple of Swami Rama of the Himalayas and has been trained in the wisdom lineage of the Himalayan Masters that involves the disciplines of meditation, spiritual wisdom

www.vikasmalkani.com
www.soulcentre.org

and yoga. A gifted orator, he is a keynote speaker at many international conferences and summits. He leads life-transforming workshops for adults and is also the creator of the SoulKids™ programme for children, which has made thousands of confident and creative children worldwide.

Vikas Malkani has been interviewed in many international newspapers and magazines and been a guest on numerous television and radio shows. His writings on self-awareness and spiritual wisdom appear regularly in magazines on yoga, holistic health and the spa industry. His television show airs on prime time every night on a national spiritual channel in India.

The Little Manual of
ENLIGHTENMENT
7 Valuable Tips for
Those in Search of
Awareness
Vikas Malkani

The Little Manual of
MEDITATION
15 Effective Ways
to Discover Your
Inner Self
Vikas Malkani